MULTIPLE MINI INTERVIEWS FOR UK MEDICAL SCHOOL

The Essential Guide
To
Multi Mini Interviews (MMI)

Over 300 questions
analysed and answered.
This unique and most up to date MMI Book
is specific for UK Medical Schools.

Marian Coll M.A.
CEO, Fast Track Medical

MULTIPLE MINI
INTERVIEWS FOR
UK MEDICAL SCHOOL

Published by Fast Track Medical
34 Shepherds Hill, Highgate, London N6 5AH

A catalogue record of this book is available from the British Library.

ISBN 978-0-9926846-1-7

Printed and bound by CPI Group (UK) Ltd, Croydon, CR0 4YY

Fast Track Medical offers One-to-One Interview Coaching for those wishing to enter medical, dental, pharmacy and vetinary schools.

Multi Mini Interviews (MMI) and group interviews are used in most medical schools. We closely monitor the questions asked each year and will help you structure excellent responses to those type of questions. We interview you in a formal setting to simulate the real interview. We provide unlimited support to you after the sessions.

Coaching is provided as follows:

- Face-to-face or by Webcam (Skype) coaching is provided by specialists in Medical School Interviews. This can be offered via SKYPE for international students and UK students
- Choice of one, two or three-hour sessions
- Personal statement should be sent in advance for review
- We analyse your personal statement, prepare tailored detailed questions, and ask those questions during the session
- You can audio record several mini-mock interviews with us, and use these to discuss and improve your performance.
- One-to-one allows us to concentrate solely on you, your personal statement and on your chosen medical schools.
- You will learn to appreciate how important it is to consider the arguments both for and against an issue.

Book now through our website: www.fasttrackmedical.co.uk
www.fasttrackdentistry.co.uk

Or call us on 07708 352315 for more information.

Acknowledgment: In order to write this book, I needed help from many sources. I thank the medical schools for all their help in answering my questions. I thank all my students who emailed me the questions after each interview. I thank all the doctors who helped me so much. A special thanks to John,Jenny, Liz, Nick, Mary, Colin, Shanthi, Fusun, Kasia, Diana, Sara and Lia for their help and encouragement

Disclaimer

TABLE OF CONTENTS

ANNEXES

CHAPTER 1

INTRODUCTION

Over 30,000 individuals apply to UK medical school every year, and only one third of applicants gain places.

It takes more than academic and extracurricular prowess to get into medical school.

The application process is a chess game and to play it well requires foresight, dedication, and strategy.

Each section of the book discusses the challenges unique to that section. We will take you through the ups and downs of what you are about to experience. We will highlight the critical aspects of the journey, steer you around the pitfalls, and help you gain insight into what matters.

The aim of this book is to equip you with the essential skills to tackle any ethical/role play questions asked at a Multiple Mini Interview (MMI), putting you ahead of the game.

Our mission is to prevent you from experiencing the unnecessary suffering that others have gone through.

There are over 300 questions with answers. The questions have been obtained from students who have sent them to Fast Track Medical after their interview. We have received questions from more than one candidate, so there are far more questions listed than you would expect to be asked at a single interview.

This book is intended to guide school leavers, graduates/postgraduates, Oxbridge and international students through the entire process.

During my extensive experience in preparing people for medical school interview, I have seen many students turn from a rambling, inconcise person into a confident, motivated, concise student which gives them the ability to win a place in medical school.

This book contains the most up to date, most candid information about medical schools, what they are looking for and the interview process. The bulk of material in this book comes from six main sources:

- My extensive experience training people for medical school interviews.
- Information gathered from students who have attended interviews.
- Information gathered from medical school admissions.
- Over 25 years interviewing medical staff for Grosvenor Medical (a renowned medical agency).
- Detailed knowledge of what happens behind the scenes of the medical school admissions.
- Fast Track Medical extensive research into the Multiple Mini Interview.

The greatest hindrance to the applicant is the interview process. You must spend time diligently preparing so that you can reduce the level of unpredictability and variability in the Multiple Mini Interview (MMI).

This book will completely prepare you for each aspect of the medical school interview. Interviewing is akin to any other activity; practice makes perfect. You cannot leave anything to chance, so prepare and study diligently. The worst thing would be to assume it would be possible to just walk in, without preparation, and nail the interview.

By following the steps outlined in this book, you can bring out your best qualities and increase your chances of getting into medical school.

The overriding question every admissions committee member is trying to answer during the course of the interview is "is this person one of us"? They are asking themselves "Do I see this individual as a Doctor"?

Our key objective is to help you receive an offer of a place to study medicine.

Let me show you the inside secrets. The book is designed to cover each of the stations of MMI interview with guided answers including what exactly to expect on the day, how best to prepare for it and what exactly the interviewers are looking for. I was driven to write this book after meeting students who have come to me after having failed the crucial interview.

The interviews are usually nerve racking, anxiety provoking events in applicants' lives. There are many necessary steps and hurdles to navigate in the process of gaining acceptance into medical school.

Each year, I look forward to hearing from my students and their parents with the exciting news of getting an offer and I find my work immensely rewarding.

I have three children, two of whom are doctors so I fully UNDERSTAND what you and your parents are going through.

To gain the most from this book, read it cover to cover so that you understand the complexity of the medical school admissions process and know what to expect.

In the chapters that follow we will cover all the various interview stations. The book gives a complete guide to handling Multiple Mini Interviews followed by the experiences of many candidates who applied for medicine.

Your chances of medical school admissions success will improve by learning the details of the complex admissions process and using the insider tips.

The key is making your decision an informed one. In the end, no one but you can assess your true fitness and commitment to pursue medicine.

Good luck and get in.

CHAPTER 2

THE MULTIPLE MINI INTERVIEW (MMI)

2.1 History of the MM

The MMI interview technique was developed and implemented in 2002 by McMaster University in Ontario, Canada for their M.D. programme. The MMI process has been in place at a number of medical schools throughout the United States, Canada and Australia. The MMI was introduced in an attempt to prevent the biases, expectations and influences that were known to be associated with more traditional interviews.

The MMI process has been thoroughly researched and shown to have good validity and reliability.

St George's Medical School was the first to introduce the MMI in the UK in 2010.

Most medical schools in the UK have now altered their admissions process by replacing the traditional applicant interview with the Multiple-Mini Interview (MMI). The MMI format is different from the traditional interview. Two of the interview stations may question areas which are more common with traditional interviews. MMI resembles speed dating, with applicants rotating through numerous interview stations, where they act out different scenarios. The MMI is similar to an objective structured clinical examination (OSCE) used in medical schools.

2.2 What is the MMI?

The MMI is a timed circuit of short interviews with scripted questions. Instructions are announced over an intercom. The scenarios are posted outside the door on a clipboard. After two minutes, the candidate is prompted to enter the room and start a five minute scenario. There is then a two minute break between stations. This cycle is repeated until every candidate has gone through all stations. The interview is conducted consecutively in each separate interview room. The process is completed in around 40 minutes and is designed to measure character and critical thinking skills rather than scientific knowledge. The goal is to pick out the best future doctors.

There are between four and twelve timed stations which applicants rotate through and no station has a weighting greater than any other.

Most of the time, stations are manned by one interviewer with all stations scoring an applicant's ability to cope with the station. All the interviewers make an independent assessment on an applicant's perceived suitability to a career in medicine. Once the applicant has completed all the stations, the scores are collated. When collated, the marks provided are used to rank candidates and inform the process of acceptance or rejection

The interviewers are often actors, medical students, doctors and members of the medical faculty. Some stations may require the candidate to interact with an actor. Candidates are presented with a scenario involving an individual, whose role is played by an actor. The candidate must confront the.person about a problem, give bad news, discuss an ethical scenario, respond to situational/behavioural type questions, research and data interpretation, critique a scenario presented in a video, or gather information. In some medical schools e.g. Queen's Medical School in Belfast, the applicant's personal statement is considered within this process.

Communication and empathetic skills are evaluated, but scientific knowledge is not assessed.

2.3   General MMI Tips for the Interview

MMI selection methods have now almost competely replaced the traditional structured interview. It is essential that you are aware of the interview format in advance so that you can adequately prepare.

- For most people the MMI interview is a white-knuckled, anxiety provoking terror session.

- Do not fear a moment or two of silence in an interview. These moments are okay, and your ability to allow them to occur projects confidence and maturity. It is almost impossible not to be nervous on interview day. You have done a tremendous amount of work to get to this point, and it is hard not to feel like your entire future may be riding in the next few hours.
- At this stage, you are academically ready for medical school, which is why you were short-listed out of a number of candidates.
- It is really important to make a good first impression. Every interviewer will be marking you on the specified task at each station. Do not forget to make eye contact and shake hands with the interviewer at each station.
- The golden rule is: if you are finding the stations difficult, other candidates are finding them difficult as well.
- You can go down on two stations and still pass the interview.
- It is important not to get bogged down on any particular station. Instead, focus on delivering a high quality and effective answer at the next station.
- It is always good to practice beforehand to calm your nerves and to build confidence and to learn to be able to talk for five minutes on a particular scenario. The more you practice, the easier it will become.
- If you are not good at thinking on your feet, it is useful to have people throw random scenarios at you, and give you a time limit, so that you get used to coming up with things to say under pressure.
- To practice the formulation of ideas, get together with some of your friends, find an article that is interesting and controversial and discuss it together, without previously researching or thinking about the ideas presented. This is to help you think quickly and efficiently and to help you formulate ideas clearly and efficiently. What is important is the articulation of ideas. Structuring your answer is of particular importance in MMIs. Some interviewers will ask only one or two questions at each station. Pause to think- even if you do know the answer.
- Some interviewers may come across as disinterested or try to make you think you are giving a bad answer. They are told to act in this manner and it doesn't have anything to do with your answers, so do not let it bother you. They will act like this to all the candidates on the day.
- Read the question carefully and decide what you are going to talk about, before entering the room. Pick out the main points and what you want to focus on. Compose your thoughts and put them into some structure that makes your answer well thought out.

- Many candidates have difficulty with time. You must practice timing the two minutes between stations so you can think and formulate how you are going to present the next one.
- Take a deep breath before you go into each room, to calm yourself.
- Most students are nervous when the bell rings for the first time, but they seem to relax as the process continues.
- Remember communication is being scored all the time.
- Try to resist simply leaping to the answer without explaining how you got there. It is very important to explain your thinking process. This allows the interviewer to see: not only what you have considered, but also how you approach an ethical scenario or problem.
- Your initial decision may be challenged. Try to defend your decisions, whilst acknowledging that the situation is difficult and conflicting views will arise.
- Nodding, hand gestures and smiling are non-verbal elements of communication that are crucial to realistic and empathetic communication.
- Your tone of voice is extremely important. Consider all the people affected by the scenario. Focus on feelings of empathy and honesty. Treat the interviewer in a warm manner and as if he is a good friend. If you do this, you will come across as genuine and caring.
- The interviewer will often hint at something and you need to pick up on these hints. They are often a crucial part of the scenario and indicate that you should explore a different area to get all the information out.
- Having the opportunity to meet several interviewers means that you have more chances to sell yourself and start fresh with each question.
- Some stations can be tougher than others, but when the buzzer goes you can start again, and the new interviewer is not aware of what you said in the other room.
- If you have a bad experience at one station, try to clear your mind and move on. It is vital that you remain positive.
- During a rest station, do not go over the previous stations in your mind.
- There are role play scenarios with an actor as well as an interviewer. In this situation, you may be asked to demonstrate communication skills through interacting with the actor, while the interviewer silently observes. DO NOT LOOK AT THE OBSERVER. Do not be put off by people making notes.
- MMI may include one or more stations with traditional interview questions such as "Why Medicine?", and lots of questions about team work and leadership.

- The interviewer sometimes probes the candidate's answers and encourages the candidate to express his or her ideas and defend them rigorously.
- Most of the scenarios tend to be deliberately ambiguous.
- During a scenario involving breaking bad news or consoling a grieving patient or relative, you may be faced with a grieving actor:
  - Stay calm. Give the patient time for a few seconds.
  - Pause while you think what to say next.
  - Do not rush to stop the crying.
  - "I can see you are upset. That's quite understandable, given what's happened".
  - Carry on communication in an appropriate empathetic tone. Ask them "How are you feeling"?
  - Concentrate on the patient's feelings at this moment. Encourage them to tell you whether they are sad, frustrated, angry or frightened.
  - Do not assume you know how they are feeling.
  - "Would you like some tissues or a drink"?
  - "Would you like some time before we talk further"?
  - "Is there anything else bothering you that you have not told me"?
  - "Is there anyone else you would like to talk to"?

Do not tell the patient to stay calm or not to worry or that everything will be ok. The aim is to understand the patient's current predicament and show some empathy. You are dealing with uncertainty. Do not offer inappropriate reassurance. The results may be bad. Do not say "I know what you are going through", because you do not.

The Stations are testing the following Skills:

- Empathy
- Initiative and resilience
- Communication and problem-solving skills
- Team work
- Insight and integrity
- Compassion
- Knowledge of health care issues
- Ethical decisions
- Current events
- Maturity and self-awareness
- Commitment to medicine

- Respect for diversity (race, religion, disability, gender, socio-economic)
- Sensitivity to the needs of others and ability to establish rapport
- How you demonstrate insight
- Effective decision making, leadership
- Maturity and self-awareness
- Commitment to Medicine
- Self-directed learner
- Understanding of the role of health professionals in society
- Data Interpretation

2.4   What to do on the Day of the Interview

- Arrive early for interview, so that you have plenty of time to prepare yourself and to hand in the necessary documentation.
- It does not reflect well if you arrive short of breath and sweating, having just got lost and had to run half a mile.
- Be positive and confident.
- Do not rush into answering a question. When you are asked a question, take a second or two before you start, even if it is something you can answer easily and you have prepared, Maintain good eye contact.
- If they ask you if you have any questions, always say no. Most of your questions should be answered on the web site.
- During the interview, if you hear bells or other people answering questions in other rooms, do not be put off. Keep talking until someone tells you that the interview has finished. Avoid fidgeting.

2.5   How to Approach the MMI Questions

Questions take a variety of forms and are designed to elicit the above information from you.

Work though the following:

- After reviewing the question, try to identify why you are being asked this question. What do you think the interviewer is trying to evaluate?
- When entering each station, pause to introduce yourself (unless instructed otherwise), smile, and consider your body language.
- What qualities will the question allow you to demonstrate?

- How can you show that you possess these qualities?
- What will you do once you enter the room?
- What factors would you consider when answering the question?
- How would you respond if you are challenged?
- How would you respond if the actor starts crying? Some of the actors employed by medical schools are professional actors.
- What steps would you take to solve the problem?
- Your ability to convey your ideas clearly and concisely.
- The GOLDEN RULE is: if a colleague is causing problems, you should always discuss the matter with them first.
- Be open and acknowledge there is a problem.
- Tackle the problem early.
- Avoid being confrontational and judgemental.
- Be supportive in helping the person to accept their problem and to find practical solutions e.g. counselling and mentoring.
- Decide together upon the best course of action and how to take it forward.
- When dealing with bad situations (such as a drunk doctor, a third year medical student cheating, plagiarism, taking drugs, doctor not performing at work, doctor arrogant and rude to the nurses), the key is to explore the reasons behind the individual doctor's actions, with sensitivity and understanding.
- Try to understand what he is going through and how overwhelming it is for him.
- Be respectful.
- You can supply emotional support.
- Your first approach to resolving any conflict should be a direct and honest conversation with the individual.
- Try to initiate the discussion in a private and non-confrontational way.
- Make the person feel listened to.
- The interviewers are testing: your ability to lead a difficult discussion, your sensitivity and ability to empathise.
- If you have good reason to believe that a colleague may be putting patients at risks, patient safety is more important than anything else. Think of the consequences they may have on the patients.
- At MMI interviews, students invariably forget that third year medical students are on the wards and forget to mention patient safety.
- The interviewers are testing your ability to listen and understand instructions and your ability to give clear instructions e.g. challenges such as, "explain how you tie a shoe lace", or "describe this picture to me"

- Sometimes the picture is a scene. Describe what is happening rather than describe the history or background information.
- Another example: "describe a room or yourself to a blind person". It is important to clarify whether the person has been blind from birth. If not, he will have memory of colours etc.

2.6 Some feedback from medical schools for candidates who were unsuccessful at MMI and Traditional Interviews

- Did not demonstrate the necessary communication skills
- Too nervous to communicate answers
- Did not expand enough on answers or give examples
- Did not know the realities of medicine
- Did not understand the role of a doctor
- Appeared unsympathetic or unemotional
- Did not demonstrate the ability to tolerate stress
- Did not demonstrate insight and empathy
- Did not have enough work experience and had not thought enough about what they learnt during that time
- Failed to listen to the questions and respond appropriately
- Did not understand the questions
- Answers were rambling or not logical.
- The applicant was arrogant.
- Not listening to the question and giving an already prepared answer, rather than thinking about what was asked and reflecting on it.
- Being either monosyllabic or rambling. You are expected to develop ideas, to elaborate, to be logical and to give evidence in your response.
- Not having fully researched the career, and not appearing to have thought deeply about the positive and negative aspects of the job. In a few cases, the applicant had no relevant experience, or had very limited experience.
- Did not use relevant experience to learn about himself/herself, the needs of patients and the kind of work that doctors and other healthcare workers do.
- Did not have any knowledge about recent events.
- Did not establish good rapport.
- Lack of knowledge about the medical school.
- Not expressing himself or herself clearly, not using his or her own ideas, not being able to think on his feet.

CHAPTER 3

MMI STATIONS

The various MMI stations are covered in the following Chapters, as follows:

In addition, information about individual medical schools are set out in Chapter 19, and a list of further general questions are set out in Annex 7.

CHAPTER 4

MMI PRIORITISATION STATION

You will be asked to list tasks in order of importance/priority, then justify your chosen sequence with an explanation for each.

When completing such a task, you should remember that your explanations for the prioritisation are more important than the actual order you generate.

There are usually no right or wrong answers.

CHAPTER 5

MMI GROUP TASK STATION

Group tasks have been used as part of a selection process for medical school applicants for some time. They are often the least popular part of the selection process. You must understand what the assessors are looking for. Thinking, in advance, of an approach to the task, will give you the best chance to succeed.

Usually, there are eight people in the group and three assessors sitting around the edge of the room making notes.

Small groups of candidates are asked to work together to deal with a recent topical scenario, e.g. "should patients be allowed bariatric surgery in the NHS?"

It is important to know what is happening and be up to date on the latest discussions. Effective preparation will give you the edge over your competitors.

Trained assessors are allocated to observe candidates during the group exercise and they assign ratings to candidates according to their communication skills and problem-solving ability.

Typically, the discussion will last twenty minutes.

What is being tested?

- How you integrate and interact with the other group members.
- Your ability to articulate and communicate.
- Your ability to cope in a pressurised situation.
- Your teamwork and leadership skills.
- Can you think creatively?
- Your time keeping.

The Golden Rules of Group Work

- Write down the main arguments for and against.
- Be friendly with the other candidates and show enthusiasm.
- Be yourself.
- Do not be put off by the assessors making notes.
- Avoid being overly competitive.
- Show you can think creatively.
- Be sensitive and tactful.
- Do not interrupt or put down other members.
- Avoid confrontation with other group members.
- Listen carefully to what others are saying.
- Do not dominate the group.
- Do not be overbearing and talk excessively.
- Avoid the temptations to act or role play.
- Contribute your own ideas effectively.
- Build constructively on the ideas of others.
- When initiating the discussion: you may say: "This is an interesting/complicated/difficult scenario". Or "I agree with what Tom and Aisha said and I would like to add ……………
- When nearing the end of the exercise say: "we have five minutes, does anyone have any other points they would like to make"?

CHAPTER 6

MMI VIDEO CRITIQUE STATION

At some MMIs, such as Queen Mary's and Warwick, as part of the assessment, you watch a ten minutes video in which you may be able to write notes. The video may relate to a GP doing a consultation with a patient.

Several factors must be taken into consideration during a consultation. Some of which include:

- introduction
- listening skills
- body language
- set up of the room
- any written communication
- any issues with consent, confidentiality, etc.
- closure of the consultation

Write down what the doctor did well and not so well.

Examples of things the doctor did well:

- The doctor explained the interpretation of the patient's results without use of jargon.
- The doctor checked, in a non-patronising way, that the patient understood.
- The doctor explained what the next steps would be and involved the patient in the decision making.
- The doctor summarised the information again at the end of the consultation.
- The doctor gave the patient time to ask questions, without interrupting him.
- The doctor had a holistic approach.

Examples of things the doctor did not do so well:

- The doctor did not have much clarity, and it seemed as though he had not thought through, in advance, what he was going to say to the patient.
- The history seemed very rushed.
- There was a lack of privacy.
- The doctor's bleep/mobile kept going off repeatedly during the consultation.
- The doctor did not identify the patient's emotion.
- The doctor did not respond appropriately to the patient's emotion.
- The patient became distressed as a result of information imparted during the consultation.
- The doctor's arms were folded.
- The doctor was too close to the patient.
- The doctor kept interrupting the patient.
- The doctor spoke to the patient in a condescending manner.
- The doctor did not give the patient sufficient time to read the consent form and ensure their understanding before asking him to sign it.
- The patient seemed confused and overwhelmed.
- The doctor did not show any empathy.
- The doctor used multiple and confusing questions/statements.
- The doctor did not address the patient's needs.
- The doctor did not seem to establish a rapport with the patient.
- The doctor did not inspire confidence and trust.

CHAPTER 7

ETHICAL DILEMMAS STATION

Ethics form part of the MMI interview. This Section deals with how to take a balanced and analytical approach to ethical problems.

There are four ethical principles of medicine:

(a)   <u>Autonomy</u>
      This relates to the patient's individual dignity, and is about respect for the individual and their ability to make decisions with regard to their own health. It includes the right to treatment, the choice of treatment and the right to refuse treatment. A competent patient can always refuse treatments. They cannot insist on a treatment that a doctor feels can cause harm.

(b)   <u>Beneficence</u>
      This states that the doctor should always act in the patient's best interests. This relates to doing the greatest good, whilst balancing risk and benefits. Doctors have an obligation to benefit the patient.

(c)   <u>Non-maleficence</u>
      This states that the doctor do no harm to the patient. Doctors must avoid causing harm and strive to protect the patient from harm.

(d)   <u>Justice</u>
      This relates to fairness, equitable use of resources and equal access to care. Individuals or groups should be similarly treated, and there should be awareness that an individual's treatment may affect the well-being of someone else as a consequence of scarce resources. The NHS has limits on the amount of money that can be spent. By spending a large amount of money on a single person, less money remains to be spent on others. NICE (The National Institute of Clinical Excellence) make choices of how the budget is spent.

Ethical dilemmas originate when there is a clash between two or more of the above principles. **Examples of 41 such ethical dilemmas follow, and for ease of reference, they are listed in Annex 1 to this book:**

1 **MMI Ethical Dilemma: Notifiable disease**

Mr Brown is a local butcher who is married with four children. Mr Brown comes to see you, his GP, after having diarrhoea for one week. A stool sample has grown campylobacter, which is a notifiable disease (Public Health (Control of Diseases) Act 1984 (Notifiable Diseases). He wants to go back to work immediately because he needs the money.

The ethical issues are:

- Autonomy
  Mr Brown has the right to make informed decisions about his care. He has a right to confidentiality, but his illness may harm his family and others. Campylobacter is a notifiable disease so, as a doctor, you are required by law to notify the Health Protection Agency. In this case, the duty to protect public health outweighs the duty to maintain patient confidentiality.

- Non-maleficence
  Explain the position to Mr Brown. He has a notifiable disease, which you must report, and, if he returns to work, he may harm the public, he could lose his job and the butcher shop could be fined and closed down. Educate Mr Brown about his condition and the reason why campylobacter is a notifiable disease and why it must be reported to the Health Inspector. The Health Inspector needs to find out who is supplying the meat and investigate the source. Acknowledge Mr Brown's anger and frustration of having to close down his butcher shop. Encourage Mr Brown to go to Social Services, as he may be eligible for financial assistance. Obviously, he would be concerned about losing customers and income. After explaining everything to Mr Brown, you hope he would stay off work and allow you to report the illness. If he refuses, you still have to breach confidentiality and inform the Health Inspector.

2 MMI Ethical Dilemma: Assisted Suicide/Euthanasia

Tony Nicklinson is a 57-year-old male with locked-in-syndrome due to a stroke in 2005. He describes his life as intolerable and his only method of communication is via an eye-blink computer. He wants the doctors to kill him, with his consent, so that they are not charged with his murder. Tony cannot travel to Switzerland for an assisted suicide, as he is physically not able to take the fatal drug himself. A barrister has said that the court should not intervene and this is not a matter that should be discussed on a case-by-case basis. Only Parliament would be able to design a system with appropriate safeguards and conditions in place.

What are your thoughts on this case?

This article is about assisted suicide, effectively a situation where an individual takes an action to commit suicide, with the help of a second party, without which, the action would not have been possible. According to the Suicide Act 1961, assisted suicide is illegal. Assisted suicide has become a very controversial issue over the past few years.

There are two main issues posed by Tony Nicklinson, as far as the medical profession is concerned: Legalising assisted suicide, and the involvement of doctors in the process:

There are several arguments **against** assisted suicide:

- Nial Dickson, chief executive of GMC, states that assisted suicide is illegal, and doctors should have no part in it.
- The fitness of doctors to practice will also be considered, if they even give information about assisted suicide. For example, about the Swiss connection.
- Licensing assisted suicide will be a very dangerous step because it will remove an essential protection for both doctors and patients. Doctors could face murder charges and prosecution by relatives or the police.
- It is also a concern that by involving doctors in the process, doctors may be encouraged to take shortcuts in care and follow the wishes of more and more patients seeking assisted suicide, because it would free up resources and beds. Financial pressures would have a big impact.
- People against assisted suicide also argue that, even if someone has expressed the wish for assisted suicide, people may change their mind later and may not be able to express their change of decision.

- It needs to be taken into account that patients can make irrational decisions when in distress or under pressure by relatives, and in some cases, if the case is not clear-cut, relatives may face murder charges e.g. by following a complaint by other relatives.
- In some cases, patients may also not have the mental capacity to make a decision for themselves.

The main arguments **in favour of** assisted suicide are:

- If the patient has mental capacity, and the decision is voluntary, and is a settled and informed decision, it needs to be respected. It is similar to withdrawing treatment for a competent patient who wishes to die,(because this will avoid a long unnecessary suffering period for the patient and enable them to die with dignity, at the time of their choosing).
- The patient's autonomy is also important and it needs to be respected. If the patient has the mental capacity to make an informed decision to die, it should be respected.
- However, the issue is not only of legalising assisted suicide, but also the issue of the role doctors will play in the process.
- It would be better if the patient who wishes to die goes through a tribunal with relatives. Maybe a legal expert and the family's doctor, familiar with the patient's illness, can ensure that the patient is not under pressure. This will make the case transparent, and avoid accusations, and protect the doctor who would otherwise be classified as a murder suspect.
- Tony Nicklinson decided to starve himself to end his life. He felt he had no other option. In fact, he contracted pneumonia and died. Perhaps it would have been more humane to end his suffering by assisted suicide.
- It is unlikely that a judge will rule in favour of patients in such scenarios because assisted suicide is illegal under the 1961 Suicide Act, and the GMC strongly opposes even giving advice to patients in favour of assisted suicide.
- Most doctors would be reluctant to offer help on assisted suicide. They are not protected, and risk dismissal from the GMC, and risk being charged with murder.

Conclusions:
- The Law and the GMC may need to address assisted suicide in certain cases. It should be tightly regulated, and addressed to a clearly defined group of terminally ill patients, or patients with intolerable suffering,

who have the mental capacity and are not being pressurized to end their lives.

- There needs to be a clear, informed intention by the patient or an advanced directive. An assessment by two doctors to confirm that the patient's condition is not going to improve and the patient should perhaps do the act (by pressing a button by any means of communication) to reduce the involvement of doctors by as much as possible.
- A doctor has both duty of beneficence and non-maleficence towards his patient and these ethical principles clash in this issue of assisted suicide. Before thinking of the involvement of doctors in assisted suicide, we need to decide whether the doctor's role is to prolong life or to end suffering by helping to end life.
- This is a very controversial topic, and it would be difficult to give a right or wrong answer without upsetting half the population. The law must prevent misuse of assisted suicide. We must also note what happened in Oregon, where suicide has gone up by 4 times after the legalization of assisted suicide. With proper regulations, people like Tony Nicklinson can die with dignity and avoid unnecessary suffering.

This scenario presents many ethical questions, the main one being whether euthanasia should be legalised. When considering the arguments for the legalisation of euthanasia, the following questions should be considered:

- Does the patient have mental capacity to make this decision?
- Do we respect the patient's own view on what is in their best interests (autonomy)? Is the patient terminally ill, or is there a possibility of recovery? How do we objectively measure a patient's suffering?

Arguments **in favour of** euthanasia:

- According to the basic ethical principle of autonomy, a patient should be allowed to determine what is in his own best interests, given they have the mental capacity to do so. Denying a patient euthanasia is like denying them their autonomy.
- Legalisation of euthanasia would end the immense suffering of terminally ill patients with illnesses such as locked-in syndrome.
- As described by Mr Nicklinson, living with locked-in syndrome can be extremely frustrating as it is very difficult to communicate or express yourself and your needs.

- Patients are able to die with dignity without dying by starvation or dehydration. When Mr Nicklinson's appeal was turned down, he refused to eat and died a week later from pheumonia.
- Putting in place proper legislation to regulate euthanasia is better than having no rules at all. Euthanasia takes place regardless of whether it is legal or not, so having a system by which to recognise patients eligible for euthanasia and strict rules on the pathway to euthanasia, will both ease suffering and prevent euthanasia from taking place incorrectly.
- It takes a lot of the NHS resources to provide care for people with terminal illnesses, e.g. regular medications to alleviate pain, and the equipment and community support needed to allow these patients to spend the last parts of their lives at home. Legalisation of euthanasia would help free up these resources.

Arguments **against** euthanasia:
- A basic medical principle is that doctors are 'preservers of life'. The idea of doctors actively causing the death of patients seems morally unacceptable and against this principle.
- Legalisation of euthanasia may take the focus and drive away from putting efforts into medical research to find cures for terminal illnesses. It may also affect the quality of palliative care available to patients. For patients like Mr Nicklinson, building more effective tools of communication and interaction, so they can live with their disability, may change their opinion that life is not worth living.
- Doctor's decisions may be affected: they may not make all the effort to provide treatment, i.e. they may take the decision to end someone's life too quickly, before considering other options. Their decisions may be financially driven (they may choose euthanasia when the cost of palliative care is too high). This will also affect the trust that patients place in doctors.
- There is no safe or accurate way to measure suffering. The only way a doctor can assess a patient's degree of suffering is through subjective reports by the patient himself. A patient in pain who is anticipating a long and painful death will report high levels of suffering. However, the patient's opinion may change with time and as his symptoms are relieved. Also, what is 'intolerable' for one patient may not be the same for another. This makes it very difficult to regulate euthanasia as each case must be considered individually.
- In cases where a patient is unable to express himself, relatives or doctors may make assumptions on what the patient 'would have

wanted'. This introduces the risk of patients who wanted to live being wrongly euthanized: involuntary euthanasia. This is a slippery slope that cannot be avoided, as it would be difficult to prove that a patient has been forced into the decision.

- Another argument is that new research is always taking place and one day a cure or treatment may be found for these patients, so it would be wrong to euthanize when there is the possibility of recovery. For example, people have been known to recover from locked in syndrome.

3 MMI Ethical Dilemma: Prescribing Oral Contraceptive Pill

You are a GP and a 14-year-old girl comes to see you in the surgery, on her own, requesting a prescription for the oral contraceptive pill. She doesn't want her parents to know.

What are the issues here?

- Establish rapport and give her support. The principles of autonomy suggest that you respect the wishes of the girl but this comes into conflict with the principles of justice, which involves the protection of vulnerable individuals.
- Check if she is Gillick competent.
- Discuss the emotional and physical implications of sexual activity including the risk of pregnancy and sexual transmitted infections.
- Give her time to make an informed choice.
- Try to establish the identity of her partner, to make sure she is not in an abusive relationship. The GMC guidance makes it clear that it is important to be vigilant for factors that might suggest the patient is involved in abusive or seriously harmful sexual activity.
- Be concerned that the relationship may be abusive and you may need to balance the benefits of knowing a sexual partner's identity against the potential loss of trust in asking for such information.
- Your patient may be involved in abusive or seriously harmful sexual activity and you would share the information with the social services or the police.
- Try to encourage her to involve her parents in the decision to start contraception.
- If she refuses, you have to respect her wishes.
- The duty of confidentiality owed to a young person is the same as that owed to any other person.

4 MMI Ethical Dilemma: Treatment of Obese/Smokers

Some NHS Trusts are refusing to put obese patients and patients who smoke on the waiting list, until they give up smoking and lose weight.

What are your views on this?

Is it wrong to deny treatment because of a 'lifestyle' factor? The decision taken by the doctor has to be the best clinical one, and it has to be taken individually. It is morally wrong to deny care on any other grounds. Smokers have paid enormous sums in taxation on cigarettes over the years. Obese patients and smokers have paid money through their national insurance. The question of whether or not the patient has surgery, and when, should be one for him, not the NHS.

Consider the smoker, his upbringing, peer group pressure, and perhaps genetic factors predisposing him to an addictive behaviour. These may combine to make him more likely to smoke.

Furthermore, he may have become addicted to smoking when a teenager. Would it be right to hold him responsible for the health consequences of his smoking as an adult 20 years later?

This raises wider issues about how we tackle our obesity epidemic in the UK. Most obesity starts in childhood and adolescence. Most smokers start smoking in adolescence.

School nurses and nurses working in a GP practice should educate children and adults on the reality of the health risks involved. They should be told that being obese could have an impact on the success and recovery from an operation, e.g. Hip Replacement.

The doctor should have an in depth conversation with the patient making sure that the patient understands the risks of having the surgery. He should enlist the help of professionals, such as nutritionists and behaviour-therapists, to encourage the patient to exercise and eat a balanced healthy diet.

Look at the underlying causes of obesity:

- A patient's thyroid gland may be under performing, leading to obesity.
- Some people will learn to comfort eat under times of stress and pressure.
- A patient may be over weight because they have a condition, which limits the exercise they can do and, despite eating a reasonable diet, cannot shed pounds.
- It may be an undesired consequence of some genetic or physiological disorder in some obese individuals.

5 MMI Ethical Station: Obese Patient Demanding Hip Replacement

What would you do if an obese patient demanded an immediate total hip replacement, which will fail in six months?

This is a very common question asked at medical school interview.

Justice: It is wrong to deny treatment because of a lifestyle factor. The decision taken by the doctor has to be the best clinical one, and it has to be taken individually. It is morally wrong to deny care on any other grounds. It is not the role of a doctor to "play God".

On the other hand, due to obesity, the hip replacement could fail. It could be said that in a system of limited resources, we should favour the patients who have a better chance of success, as this would increase the overall benefit from the money spent.

This argument comes into conflict with the principles of autonomy and beneficence. Look at the underlying causes of obesity as outlined in 6 above.

To allow the doctor to fulfil both the beneficence and the non-maleficence ethical principles, it would be better to postpone the operation for 6-12 months, allowing the patient to lose weight. Have an in depth discussion with the patient to make sure she understands the consequences of obesity. Take a non-judgemental, compassionate attitude to help establish patient's trust. Enlist the help of a dietician, psychologist and a physiotherapist to devise a more structured approach.

Patient motivation for making difficult behaviour changes is a complex phenomenon that requires sensitivity, flexibility, and persistence on the part of the doctor, to effectively manage. The potency of small improvements can be increased by emphasizing more subjective measures, such as how the patient will feel after the weight loss and the hip replacement e.g. more energy, reduced fatigue, greater mobility, no pain and the ability to enjoy themselves. Establishing initially modest expectations, providing consistent feedback, monitoring adherence, and offering constructive encouragement by the whole team are elements of successful weight loss, both short term and in the long run. Ensuring the patient has appropriate pain relief during the six months period before the hip replacement is important.

Although the patient has a right to autonomy, she cannot demand treatment that is not on offer. If the risks of having the hip replacement outweigh the benefits, the doctor could refuse surgery.

Conclusion: Delay the surgery so that the patient can reduce the obesity problem and go ahead to have a more successful operation.

6 MMI Ethical Dilemma: Patient Confidentiality

You are a junior doctor and you saw the exchange between two of your friends, both junior doctors, discussing patients on a private face book group.

What would you do?

- Contact them immediately. Explain to them that they must not discuss professional experiences on line.
- Although patients are not identified by name, it is possible that they could be identified indirectly from the details given, and that would breach confidentiality.
- Explain that their exchange breached patient confidentiality and risked damaging public trust in the profession.
- Explain that it is unacceptable use of social media by a doctor.
- Recommend that they delete the conversations on face book immediately, and they must not post any further messages.

7 MMI Ethical Dilemma: Professional Boundaries

Sarah, a 16-year-old student has been admitted to accident and emergency. She has a history of eating disorders. You are the doctor looking after her. She asked you for a friend request on face book.

What would you do?

- Do not accept Sarah's request because you want to maintain the professional boundary between you. Consider the potential risks using social media and the impact that inappropriate use could have on patient trust.
- However, be concerned that Sarah is vulnerable, and may see this as rejection, which could be damaging to her. Sensitively explain that even if you are unlikely to treat Sarah again, it wouldn't be appropriate for you to be face book friends with a patient.
- Social media can blur the boundaries between a doctor's personal and professional lives and may change the nature of the relationship between a doctor and a patient.

8 MMI Ethical Dilemma: Doctor Behaviour

You are in a hospital canteen and you see three of your friends, who are junior doctors, laughing and joking about their patients and what they said to them.

As a junior doctor, what would you do?

- Speak to them immediately and ask them to stop. Explain that they are breaching patient confidentiality. If they carried on, report them to their consultant.
- The GMC states: "Doctors must not use publicly accessible social media to discuss individual patients or anyone else. You should not share identifiable information about patients when you can be overheard in a public place or in an internet chat room, unattended or where they can be seen by other patients, unauthorized healthcare staff, or the public" (Confidentiality GMC 2013)

9   MMI Ethical Station: Definition of "Competent"

Only competent patients can give consent. What is meant by 'competent'?

Competency involves the capacity for consent. The patient has mental capacity. A patient who understands the information he is given and is capable of making a rational decision out of his own accord is competent. Rules vary depending on whether the patient is an adult or a child.

<u>Adult</u>: An adult can make a Living Will. If, at any point in the future, he is no longer able to make decisions, then the doctor will have to act in the best interest of the patient. Any adult who is confused or has a severe mental disorder is not competent.

<u>Children</u> (under the age of 16 years): Are they Gillick Competent?

Children under the age of 16 years can be deemed competent to give consent, provided they are shown to be mature enough to understand the information given to them about the procedure, and its consequences. If the child (patient) is competent, the doctor should encourage the child to involve the parents/guardians. The doctor must respect the patient's decision, if he chooses otherwise. If the doctor went ahead and involved parents or guardians regardless of the patient's wishes, it would be a breach of confidentiality. If the child is incompetent, the doctor is obliged to involve his parents/guardians. If the doctor feels the child is in danger or at risk of harm, he should contact social services/the police. If both parents refuse to give consent for a lifesaving procedure, a court order can be imposed to enable the operation to take place.

10 MMI Ethical Station: Patient Choice

Do you think it is right for patients to make the choice as to what is in their own best interest?

In favour of patient choice:

- The patient should be able to make decisions about their care.
- By questioning doctors, patients ensure the provision of safer care.

Against patient choice:

- The patient may not have the background knowledge to make the best decision.
- Relatives sometimes make decisions based on unreliable information e.g. unreliable information on the Internet.

11 MMI Ethical Station: Request for Non-Conventional Treatment

What would you do if a patient came to you asking for advice about a non-conventional treatment that they found on the Internet?

Buying drugs on line may be dangerous. The patient may not have the background knowledge to make the best decisions for himself. Patients may be influenced, by friends or relatives who are not qualified to give advice. Patients may make decisions based on external information, which may not be accurate or appropriate for their situation.

Autonomy: A patient's autonomy includes the right to treatment, the choice of treatment and the right to refuse treatment. Ensure that the patient is given all the information that he needs to make an informed choice about the drug.

Beneficence: Act in the patient's best interest. This includes searching for the best treatment. Check what his expectations are, whether he is unhappy with current treatment. Be honest with the patient. A lot of therapies are advertised on line, but many have not been tested and may be unsafe. Many of these drugs do not work. If it is a medication with which you are not familiar, investigate and ask other colleagues for their opinion.

Non-maleficence: Do no harm to the patient. The possible side effects and risks of the drug have to be considered carefully. Ask the patient for the details of the website and check out the drug. Ask your colleagues, ask the hospital pharmacy, call the drug company and check the drug and its side effects. Find out if the drug is regulated, and perhaps get it analysed in the lab. Also establish how this drug works with the other drugs he is taking. Ask the patient what other drugs he is on, if they work and if he has any side effects, and why he has gone on line seeking other drugs. Discuss more conventional drugs that may be more suitable, and take a holistic approach. If the patient takes medication for depression, explain that some drugs used for depression take time to work. The patient may not aware of this.

Once you have presented all the facts to the patient, it is the patient's decision which drug he takes.

12 MMI Ethical Dilemma: Request for Husband's Sperm

A 35- year- old gentleman was on his way to work when he was knocked down by a car and ended up unconscious in intensive care. You are the F1 doctor and his wife comes to see her husband and tells you she wants his sperm.

What are the ethical issues here?

This is a very complicated question and it raises significantly different issues. You need a lot more information about the patient.

- What is his prognosis?
- Does the team think he is going to recover?
- The patient does not have decision making capacity and he cannot give consent.
- What about the welfare of the child to be?
- It has a major implication for his wife's future and for the future of his potential child.
- Determine if he had signed an advanced directive that he would want to father a child, while he was unconscious, or after his death.
- If there was no advance directive, check with his GP, if he was planning to pursue in-vitro fertilisation treatment. His willingness to undergo infertility testing and their plan to pursue in-vitro fertilisation suggest that this patient had a strong desire to have a child. While this evidence gives some guidance to his desire, it provides no indication of his wishes about his wife having this child after his death.
- His views, on the wellbeing of a child raised by a single parent, are likewise unknown.
- Is his wife's intense desire to have her husband's offspring morally relevant, and if it is, is it sufficient to justify the removal of semen without his explicit consent? His wife is probably in a state of shock and could be desperate to hold on to her husband's sperm, without thinking of the consequences.
- Discuss this with the rest of the team and the legal team.

Conclusions
- If the patient had a clear written advanced directive that he would want to father a child if he was unconscious or after his death, it would be ok to consent to his wife having his sperm.
- If there is no advance directive, the request should be declined. While the decision might intensify the grief of his wife, it is ethically wrong to allow her to have his sperm without his consent.

13 MMI Ethical Dilemma: Request for Expensive Prescription

Helen is looking for a particular painkiller. Her GP refuses as he says it is too expensive. What are the issues here?

Autonomy: This gives Helen the right to refuse treatment but not the right to have treatment not on offer.

The doctor has a duty to act in the best interest of a patient (beneficence) and not to harm the patient (non-maleficence).

Beneficence: this considers balancing the benefits of giving the painkillers against the cost. Is the doctor giving the painkillers to some patients and not to others, or is he not prescribing the painkillers to any patient, because they are too expensive? The doctor must not feel pressurised to prescribe drugs he does not agree with. The doctor and patient should form a therapeutic relationship, where the patient needs to feel understood by her doctor and trust her doctor.

Justice: distributing benefits, risks and costs fairly. Patients in similar positions should be treated in a similar manner. NICE (National Institute of Clinical Excellence) recommends which treatment are to be prescribed and sets limits on how much it considers reasonable to spend, even if the more expensive treatment is better. It uses QALYs (quality added life years). If the treatment is more expensive than the standard treatment and is not much better than the standard treatment, it can be said to be unreasonable to expect the NHS to fund such treatment.

Conclusion: there is a possible conflict between the ethical principles of autonomy on one side and beneficence/non maleficence/justice on the other. The doctor must explain the position to the patient and encourage her to accept the drugs on offer.

14 MMI Ethical Dilemma: Disclosure of Diagnosis

You are a junior doctor. Mr Ilkow is an 82- year- old Polish gentleman on your ward. He was diagnosed with advanced carcinoma. Before you tell Mr Ilkow his diagnosis, his daughter stopped you in the ward and says: "If my father has cancer, please do not tell him as he would not be able to cope with the news".

What are the ethical issues in this scenario?

- Protecting the patient's confidentiality.
- Mental capacity of Mr Ilkow.
- Family dynamics and culture.

Autonomy: Mr Ilkow has the right to make his own treatment decisions about his health care. Everyone is assumed to have mental capacity to make decisions, unless it is proven otherwise. This would include Mr Ilkow deciding not to know his diagnosis, if he chose not to. He may not want his family to know his diagnosis. Explain to the daughter that you cannot discuss her father's diagnosis without his permission.

Beneficence: The daughter is asking you to withhold the truth from the patient, because she has his best interest at heart. She wants to spare her father the potentially painful experience of hearing difficult news. If the father gives you permission to tell his daughter the bad news, have a thoughtful discussion with her and reassure her that disclosure of the news to her father will be done sensitively.

Non-maleficence: Check if Mr Ilkow is competent and check his level of English to see whether he needs an interpreter. If he is competent and he wants to know his diagnosis, tell him. Tell Mr Ilkow all the relevant aspects of his illness. Complete and truthful disclosure is important. Appropriate sensitivity to the patient's culture and ability to digest bad news is also important. Ask Mr Ilkow if you can discuss his diagnoses with his daughter and, if so, whether he would rather you did so in front of him, or with his daughter alone. If he wants you to tell his daughter alone, make an appointment to see her in your office to discuss his diagnosis. If Mr Ilkow is not competent, check if his daughter has lasting power of attorney to make medical decisions on his behalf. Also, look into any cultural issues for Mr Ilkow and his family.

15 **MMI Ethical Station: Abortion**

What are your views in relation to abortions?

In the UK, abortion is governed by the Abortion Act 1967. Pregnancy can only be legally terminated up to 24 weeks of gestation.

Ethical issues in support of abortions:

Autonomy: Some people take the view that abortion is a woman's right to exercise control over her own body. However, this raises the question; is the foetus not a person with his own rights, too?

Beneficence: Abortions will always be sought by women who are desperate, and it is better to have safe termination services, rather than unregulated abortion. Termination of pregnancy may be necessary: when the pregnancy may cause permanent injury to the physical or mental health of the pregnant woman; when continuance of the pregnancy may involve greater risk to the life of the pregnant woman than the risk of abortion; and if there is substantial risk that the child will suffer from physical or mental abnormalities and be seriously handicapped. Abortion is also permitted when rape, mental illness and health reasons are issues.

Ethical issues against abortions:

Non-maleficence: Many who challenge abortion do so because of their view that abortion challenges the sanctity of human life.

Justice: Some people say abortion is used as a means of contraception, and that it also encourages some people to be irresponsible with contraception methods. By permitting abortion, the respect society feels for other vulnerable humans may be diminished. The availability of abortion may promote irresponsible attitudes to unprotected sex, e.g. leading to a rise in sexually transmitted infections. For some women, having an abortion may cause psychological problems in the future.

16 MMI Ethical Dilemma: Right to Die

Mrs King, aged 60, has metastatic lung cancer and lives at home with her husband. She has difficulty breathing and has a drip of diamorphine for pain relief. You are her GP, and on your visit to her she said: "I am in terrible pain and I am such a burden to my poor husband. Please help me to die".

What are the ethical issues here?

- Discuss the problem with Mrs King and empathize with her.
- Is Mrs King competent?
- Is there a risk that Mrs King may commit suicide?
- Does she want her husband to know about her position, and to involve him in the discussion, or not?
- What drugs is she taking and what dosages?
- Are the drugs causing or contributing to her depression?
- How long has she had this desire to die?
- What is the husband's situation, and is he aware of his wife's desire to die, or has he put pressure on his wife to seek assisted suicide?

Autonomy: Autonomy depends on the patient being competent. If Mrs King has the ability to understand her situation and the full implications of what she is saying, her autonomy should be respected. Acknowledge Mrs King's concerns and anxieties, and discuss her situation with her. Patients who are dying should be afforded the same respect and standard of care offered to all other patients.

Non-maleficence: Cause no harm to Mrs King. Explain to Mrs King that euthanasia is illegal in the UK.

Discuss with Mrs King her options, so that she makes an informed choice, and speak to the rest of the team. She may be depressed and may benefit from anti-depressants.

- Increase her dosage of diamorphine, to try and relieve her pain.
- If she is concerned about her husband being exhausted, talk to the different teams to arrange more support.
- Macmillan Nurses could come in every day to look after her.
- Respite care and home help could be arranged to give her husband a break.

- Encourage her to chat to her husband and the rest of the family.
- Emphasise the services that hospice can offer her and her family.
- The GMC (2013) indicates: "Where the likely progression of a patient's condition is known, and their death is seen as an inevitable outcome, it is important to ensure that the patient's palliative or terminal care needs are identified and met appropriately"
- Conclude the conversation by reinforcing your commitment to care for the patient and family regardless of the decision they make. Act with the best interest of the patient and ensure she is treated with dignity and compassion.

17 MMI Ethical Dilemma: Surrogacy

Mr and Mrs Brown enter into a surrogacy arrangement with Ms O'Brien. Mr Brown's sperm is used in artificial insemination. When the baby is born, Ms O'Brien no longer wishes to give the child to Mr and Mrs Brown. Mr and Mrs Brown have paid £50,000 for her surrogacy services.

What are the ethical issues here?
Under English Law, the legal mother of a child born through surrogacy, at birth, is always the surrogate mother. The law says that the woman who carries the child is the legal mother. The intended mother has no recognition as a parent, even if she is the child's biological mother. Surrogacy is not illegal in the UK, but it is restricted by various legal rules. In the UK, receiving money to participate in surrogacy is illegal.

18 MMI Ethical Dilemma: Difference of Opinion regarding Right to Live

A mother of two children entered the hospital after suffering a massive stroke and was put on a ventilator. Doctors believe that she would not regain brain function. Her son goes to the hospital first and told doctors that should his mother suffer heart failure or any other irreversible complications, no measures should be taken to safeguard her life. Her daughter arrives and claimed that her brother was not interested in helping their mother. She wanted to do everything possible to extend her mother's life. The mother is widowed and had not specified which of her children is to make decisions on her behalf.

What are the ethical issues here?

This is a very complicated scenario. Family disagreements and also disagreements between doctors and relatives, particularly when a terminally ill patient lacks capacity, can be very common.

Autonomy: The mother is no longer in a position to express her wishes. The past and present wishes of the patient should be taken into consideration. If the mother does not have capacity, or has not given her children a Lasting Power of Attorney, or made an Advance Directive, this makes the situation more complicated. In cases like this, the doctors have to focus on what the patient, not her children, would want. This means looking for statements that the patient may have made that gives clues about her wishes. Advance decisions do not have to be written down. If, while watching Holby City, the mother had commented that she would rather be unplugged than be kept in a vegetative state, that sentiment would hold more weight than any of her children's opinions on the matter. Everyone should be asked to contribute their recollections about her wishes. Did she express wishes about what she would want in this sort of circumstance?

Beneficence: The doctors would have to act in the best interest of the patient. It is ultimately the doctor's decision as to what her best interests are. The doctor should consult his team and the legal team. End of life discussions are difficult and the doctor should be compassionate and empathic towards the relatives. The doctor should explain carefully that there was nothing more that could be done for the mother to reverse her condition, and any interventions would be futile. In the course of the consultation, and through the doctor's good communication skills, maybe her daughter will change her mind.

Non maleficence: It is arguably harmful to keep the patient alive and the team should tell the children that Do Not Resuscitate order would be put in place. If no Lasting Power of Attorney is in place, the doctor can take into consideration their ideas. However, the doctor has no obligation to do what the children want. The doctor always has to act in the best interest of the patient.

19 MMI Ethical Dilemma: Exposure to HIV

An HIV positive patient is bleeding from a laceration and needs urgent treatment. You do not have gloves. Would you put the patient or your own safety first?

- Put your own safety first.

- If there are no gloves on the ward, give some dressings to the patient and ask him to apply pressure until you go and get gloves.

20 MMI Ethical Dilemma: Organ Transplant

You are a doctor. The parents of a child with Down's Syndrome and epilepsy are refusing an essential organ transplant for their child, and thus putting his/her life at risk. What would you say to the parents to try and convince them to allow treatment? What reasons might they have to refuse the treatment, and what actions would you take if they continued to refuse?

This is a very complicated question. The doctor has a duty to act in the best interest of the child (beneficence). And not harm the child (non-maleficence).

He would be held responsible and possibly be negligent, if he does not do the organ transplant.

How would you convince the parents?

- Ask the parents to explain what they are concerned about, and why they do not want to agree to the organ transplant. Perhaps they object on religious grounds. Or they may not wish to prolong the life of the child because the child has Downs' Syndrome and epilepsy. They may be concerned that the child may die during the operation. It is very important to establish exactly on what grounds the parents do not consent to the transplant operation.
- Check the parent's level of understanding of the child's conditions, and explain the benefits of having the organ transplant but also the risks involved in such an operation, as well as the consequences of not having the transplant e.g. deterioration in health and potentially death.
- Suggest they seek counselling and perhaps talk to a disability psychiatrist.
- It is illegal to assume that a person with learning disability is automatically incompetent (Mental Capacity Act and Mental Health Act).
- Refer the case to your supervising consultant and the legal team because this is a very serious and complicated scenario.
- If not resolved by the parents consenting, the matter may have to be resolved in court.

In a similar case, an under-aged girl refused to have a lifesaving heart transplant because she is afraid that it would turn her into another person. This went to court and she was essentially forced to have the transplant procedure done, as it was assumed that she was not competent and her reasons where irrational.

Another case involved Neon Roberts who had a brain tumour. His mother refused to consent to radiotherapy. He was made a ward of court, and the judge ruled that society could not allow his mother to refuse the treatment.

21 MMI Ethical Dilemma: Blood Transfusion

A mother comes to A&E with her seven- year- old daughter who is bleeding profusely, and refuses to allow you to administer a blood transfusion to the child. What would you do?
This was one of the most common ethical questions asked at medical school interviews last year.

- Immediately stop the bleeding, and ask the mother for her consent for a blood transfusion.
- You cannot ask the child to consent to the blood transfusion, because she is only seven and therefore not Gillick Competent.
- Ask the mother to explain what she is concerned about, and why she does not want to consent to a blood transfusion. Perhaps she is concerned about the procedure itself, or that the child will be infected by the blood e.g. AIDS, hepatitis, TB, etc.
- Or she may object on religious grounds.
- Check the mother's level of understanding of blood transfusion, and explain the reasons for having the transfusion, and the consequences of not having the transfusion e.g. death of the child.
- Explain that the blood is screened and will not harm the child.
- If the mother still refuses to give her consent, inform your team and the legal team.
- They may need to apply for a court order to proceed with the blood transfusion.
- Also try to contact the child's father and obtain his consent for the transfusion.
- However, if the child needs the blood transfusion immediately, give it without the consent of the parents.
- Act in the best interest of the patient.

22 MMI Ethical Dilemma: Disclosure of Genetic Condition

Sarah and Mary are sisters. Mary has a five-year-old son who was diagnosed with Duchene Muscular Dystrophy (DMD), which is a genetic condition. Sarah is 9 weeks pregnant. She knows her nephew has a serious genetic condition, but does not know the diagnosis. Both sisters are your patients. Sarah made it clear to you that she would terminate her pregnancy if she knew that the foetus was affected with a serious inherited condition. Mary does not get on with her sister, and she wants the information about her son to remain confidential.

What are the ethical issues here?

This is a very complicated scenario. The principles that govern genetic confidentiality within families are different. If one member of the family tests positive for a genetic disease, do you think the rest of the family deserve access to that information?

Many doctors are dividing private information into two categories: personal and joint. Parker and Lucassen (2004) propose an alternative model: the joint account model. Members of a family do have a right to some personal information that directly affects their health, just as they would have information about a jointly held bank account.

In the joint account model, the genetic information, although obtained from Mary's blood and medical history, belongs to the family. Sarah has the right to such information, as it is key information to help her to know important aspects of her genetic make-up. Mary knows something, not only about herself and her son but also about Sarah and her foetus. Mary knows that Sarah's foetus has a significant chance of suffering from Duchene Muscular Dystrophy (DMD), but Sarah does not know this. This is unfair to Sarah.

It is not clear whether failure to provide information to Sarah about her nephew, or to test her using information gained from testing him, amounts to "risk of death or serious harm".

If information that could affect other family members is uncovered during testing, you could discuss the information with your patient. If he or she does not want to pass on the diagnosis, and you know that withholding that information could cause harm to another person, you can ethically break confidentiality and disclose it.

As a doctor, you want to make sure that certain factors are met:

- Will withholding this information from Sarah cause serious harm?
- Will telling Sarah about the genetic condition prevent harm?
- Does the risk of harm to Sarah outweigh the harm of violating confidentiality?
- Discuss the situation with Mary, and encourage her to share the information with Sarah.
- If Mary does not want to tell her sister, ask Mary to allow you to share the information with her sister.
- If Mary does not want you to pass on the diagnoses, tell her that you have no choice but to break confidentiality and tell the sister.

23 MMI Ethical Station: Gillick Competence

What is Gillick Competence?

In 1985, Mrs Gillick took her Health Authority to court for supplying contraceptives to her daughter without her consent. She has five daughters and felt she had the right to know if the doctor prescribed contraceptives to them. She lost the case. The court found that a parent's right to consent to treatment on behalf of a child ends when the child has sufficient intelligence and understanding to consent to the treatment themselves. Mrs Gillick appealed to the House of Lords. Lord Fraser ruled in favour of the Health Authority.

It is for the doctor to decide whether a child has reached this level of maturity and understanding. The doctor should encourage the child to involve their parents. If she refuses, the doctor has to respect her wishes and not tell the parents.

This case led to the term: Fraser Competence or Gillick Competence. The judgement related to decisions about contraceptive treatment, but it has since been used to aid decisions about other healthcare treatment in patients under 16 years old.

Capacity is decision specific: a young person who has the capacity to consent to relatively straightforward procedures may not necessarily have the capacity to consent to complex procedures entailing high risk or serious consequences.

A Fraser or Gillick Competent child can give consent without involving the parents.

24 MMI Ethical Dilemma: Abortion

Mary is an 18-year-old girl who comes to see you, with her mother, at your GP practice. She tells you she is pregnant and doesn't know what to do. Her mother wants her to have an abortion, so she can go to University. She has a long- term boyfriend who works as a waiter and lives with his family.

What are the ethical issues here?

Confidentiality: check with Mary if she agrees to her mother being involved in the consultation. Carry out a pregnancy test and scan to confirm the age of the foetus. If Mary is over 24 weeks pregnant, abortion is not allowed.

An empathetic and non-judgemental approach in this situation is critical to establishing trust.

- Reassure Mary that you are there to help her in whatever decision she makes.
- Take a holistic approach to Mary's needs.
- Is she feeling pressurized by her mother to have an abortion?
- What about the physical impact of the abortion itself?
- What are the social consequences, including impact on her relationship with her mother and with her boyfriend?
- How will she financially support the child? The boyfriend works as a waiter and lives with his parents. This suggests he may not be able to support her.
- Where is she going to live, if her parents reject her?
- The abortion may have a psychological impact on her at a later date.

Autonomy: Mary has the right to make decisions about her healthcare. Her wishes must be respected. Give her all the options available to her. Encourage her to interrupt you at any time, to ask questions. Explain to her what an abortion is and provide her with any information that she needs.

Beneficence: You want to do what is best for Mary. If Mary has the abortion, she may regret it at a later date, and may end up with depression and guilt. If she decides to keep the baby, her future will be affected: she may not be able to continue her education or go to university, she may find it more difficult to find and keep a job, she may lose her friends, she may lose her boyfriend, and she may damage her relationship with her mother. Looking after a baby is difficult and time consuming. If Mary decides to have an abortion, her boyfriend has no right to prevent her from having one.

Give Mary all the information you think she needs to make an informed decision, and ask her to go away and consider her options. Recommend that Mary have counselling.

25 MMI Ethical Dilemma: Abortion

You are a GP. Sarah, who is a 14-year-old, comes to see you asking for an abortion.

What are the ethical issues here?

Carry out a pregnancy test to confirm she is pregnant, and a scan to confirm the age of the foetus. If she is over 24 weeks pregnant, abortion would not be allowed.

In this situation, an empathetic and non-judgemental approach is critical to establishing trust.

There are many issues to be considered:

- Check whether Sarah is Fraser competent, by checking her level of maturity and her understanding of her pregnancy.
- If Sarah is Fraser competent, explain to her that she does not have to involve her parents, if she does not wish to, but encourage her to do so, because they may give her support.
- In a sensitive and reassuring manner, stress to Sarah that you are there to help her.
- Discuss with Sarah the circumstances of how she became pregnant. Perhaps Sarah has been sexually abused or raped.
- It is also necessary to establish whether the father of the child is over 16, because that would be illegal as Sarah is only 14.

- It may be necessary to notify social services, the police, and the parents.
- If so, seek Sarah's consent to do so, but if she did not consent, explain that you would have to break confidentiality.
- Take a holistic approach to Sarah's needs.

Beneficence: You want to do what is best for Sarah. If Sarah has the abortion, she may regret it at a later date, and may end up with depression and guilt. If she decides to keep the baby, her future will be affected: she may not be able to continue her education or go to university, she may find it more difficult to find and keep a job, she may lose her friends, she may lose her boyfriend, and she may damage her relationship with her mother. Looking after a baby is difficult and time consuming. If Sarah decides to have an abortion, her boyfriend has no right to prevent her from having one. Give Sarah all the information you think she needs to make an informed decision, and ask her to go away and consider her options. Recommend that Sarah have counselling.

26 MMI Ethical Dilemma: Patient Demanding Antibiotics

You are a GP and a patient, with a viral infection, comes to see you demanding antibiotics?

What would you do?

Autonomy: The patient has the right to treatment, and the right to refuse treatment. However, antibiotics do not treat viral infection.

Beneficence: This principle emphasizes the moral importance of doing good to patients. In this situation, do not prescribe antibiotics because antibiotics do not treat viral infection. Explain to the patient that he has a viral infection and not a bacterial infection, and that antibiotics only treat bacterial infection and not viral infection. Also explain that excessive use of antibiotics increases antibiotic resistance. The cost of the use of the antibiotics to the NHS is not justified, because it is not needed. Suggest alternative treatment such as paracetamol and bed rest.

27 MMI Ethical Dilemma: Refusal to Take Medication

Mr Brown, who is 78-years-old, refuses to take his medication for heart failure following a recent heart attack. Not taking the medication exposes him to serious risks, including possible death. He presents to your surgery with his wife who wants you to talk some sense into him.

What are the ethical issues here?

One concern is confidentiality. Check with Mr Brown, if he is happy to have his wife in the consultation.

Autonomy: Mr Brown has the right to make his own decisions about his health care. You have to respect that decision.

Beneficence: Act in the patient's best interest. A holistic approach would be very much needed here. Handle this situation with sensitivity, allowing Mr Brown to talk about his reasons for not taking his medication, and consider them carefully. Look at the underlying issues:

- Physical reason: maybe they are making him sick, drowsy, loss of appetite, feeling depressed, going to the toilet all the time etc.
- Maybe his friends have told him the medication will do him more harm than good.
- Maybe he is frightened of injections.
- Psychological reasons: Is Mr Brown depressed? Maybe he has Alzheimer's and is forgetting to take his medication.
- He might need referral to a counsellor or a psychiatrist.
- If he is lacking in capacity, with his permission, involve his wife and family.
- Also involve the rest of the team, to determine the best way forward.
- Social reasons: Is he having problems living with his wife?
- Does the medication interfere with his lifestyle?

These sort of discussions are often difficult and good communications skills really become important here. Tell Mr Brown all the relevant aspects of his heart condition, expected outcomes with and without medication, and benefits of the treatment. Explain the serious risks of not taking his medication. If he refuses to take it because of the side effects, make him aware of possible alternative medication. Address the underlying issues, and propose appropriate action. If Mr Brown is competent, and wants to die, respect his decision and offer him palliative options.

28 MMI Ethical Dilemma: Vaccinations

Should vaccinations be made compulsory?

There are two main reasons for parents to get their child vaccinated:

- To prevent the child getting the disease.
- To prevent the child infecting others, and to contribute to eradicating a disease in society.

Vaccinations are an emotive subject for most parents, who are anxious not to take any risks with the health of their children. Risks from vaccinations are much smaller than the risks of large numbers not being vaccinated.

Autonomy: The parents have the right to refuse to have the child vaccinated.

Beneficence: There is overwhelming evidence that immunisations are safe.

Non-maleficence: There are small risks involved. Vaccines are not 100% safe. A parent's decision not to vaccinate their child may put others at risk.

Justice: Do parents have the right to refuse treatment for their children, even if the law allows them to? Do they have an ethical responsibility as a member of society as well as a parent? The Government must consider the potential impacts a non-vaccinated child can have on the population, given that vaccinations are not 100% effective, and a vaccinated child may still be affected by a non-vaccinated one. At the same time, acknowledge that this is a difficult issue that places the government in a tricky situation. They do not wish to legislate on this issue, but they wish to protect children from infectious diseases. The potential risks associated with an under-vaccinated population are too great to be ignored. In Wales, in April 2013, there were complaints that parents' refusals to immunize their children is responsible for the increased incidence, of over 600 cases, of Measles. After what happened in Wales, is it still fair that a parent has the right to object to vaccinating her children? By making it compulsory, vaccination saves the lives of thousands of children every year, and with cooperation we can eradicate a disease.

Conclusion: This is a very complex issue. But perhaps compulsory vaccination is not the way to go about it. Educating these parents is more likely to tackle the root of the problem, by addressing the uncertainty. Perhaps the government should introduce more health promotions, leaflets, and advice on the problems that may arise if parents do not get their children vaccinated. To force them to have their children vaccinated, affects the doctor patient relationship, and the patient's autonomy. Essentially, making anything compulsory is clearly hindering a person's right to make her own choices. On balance, it is better to leave the law as it is and put time and effort into education.

29 MMI Ethical Dilemma: Confidentiality

When would a doctor break confidentiality?

Ethical issues:

- Doctors face challenges to this long-standing obligation to keep all information between doctor and patient private. You have a duty, as a doctor, to respect the patients' trust and keep this information private.
- This requires the doctor to respect the patient's privacy, by restricting access of others to that information.
- Furthermore, creating a trusting environment, by respecting patient privacy, can encourage the patient to be as honest as possible during the course of the visit.
- Implied consent is given by the patient.
- In the course of caring for patients, the patient understands that doctors will find themselves exchanging information about patients with other doctors.
- These discussions are often critical for patient care, and are an integral part of the learning experience for medical students.
- Confidentiality is not an absolute obligation. Situations arise where the harm in maintaining confidentiality is greater than the harm brought about by not disclosing confidential information.
- In each situation, the doctor should ask whether lack of this specific information about this patient would put a specific person, you can identify, at high risk of serious harm.
- A patient who has epilepsy and continues to drive needs to be reported to the DVLA.
- Suspected cases of child abuse must be reported.
- Doctors have a duty to protect individuals from any serious threat or harm, if they have information that could prevent that harm.

- The determining factor in justifying breaking confidentiality is whether there is a good reason to believe specific individuals or groups are placed in serious danger, depending on the medical information at hand e.g. if a patient shares a specific plan, with a doctor, to harm a particular individual.

Concern for Public Welfare:

- You are required by law to report, to the Health inspector, notifiable diseases e.g. mumps, measles, tuberculosis, meningitis and many more.
- In these cases, the duty to protect public health outweighs the duty to maintain a patient's confidentiality.
- Information required by a court must be disclosed.
- If the police need information or access to medical records in the course of an investigation, this requires a court order.

30 MMI Ethical Dilemma: Blood Transfusion/Jehovah's Witness

What would you do if a known Jehovah's Witness arrived in casualty unconscious, bleeding profusely and in need of an urgent blood transfusion?

Immediately stop the bleeding.

Autonomy: Jehovah's Witnesses normally do not accept blood transfusions, believing it is unnatural and against the will of God. The patient has the right to make his own decisions about his health care, even if this defies what the doctors think is in his best interest. The patient is unconscious and cannot express his wishes or give consent.

Beneficence: Act in the best interest of the patient. Establish what is in the patient's best interest.

- Check his pocket to see if he carries a Jehovah Witness card, which confirms that he is a Jehovah Witness and will not consent to a blood transfusion.
- Check hospital records. He may be on file and his wishes may be recorded.
- Try to contact relatives to find out more information. He may have given his family an Advance Directive or Lasting Power of Attorney to make medical decisions on his behalf.

- See if there is an alternative to giving blood.
- Contact the team for advice, including the hospital legal team. If there is no information available, do not assume, just because he is a Jehovah's Witness, that he would not agree to a transfusion. Act in the best interest of the patient and give the blood transfusion.

31 MMI Ethical Dilemma: Fitness to Drive

You are a GP and one of your patients, Mr Brown, comes to see you and tells you his memory is going, and you feel he is not fit to drive. A few days later you see Mr Brown, with his wife in the car, driving erratically on the wrong side of the road.
What would you do?

Make an appointment to see Mr Brown, as soon as possible. Discuss the situation with him. Ask Mr Brown if he agrees you may discuss this matter with his wife and family.

This case highlights the number of important points that arise when a patient has to stop driving immediately. The fact that Mr Brown is the sole driver in the household will have a major impact on the family. He is an active man and drives everywhere. Being able to drive is essential for him for shopping and for going to lunch clubs for the elderly. Mr Brown will be very upset to lose his independence. Carefully support him both practically and emotionally. Speak to the family to discuss any other form of transportation available. Involve a social worker and check if they offer any other mode of transport for the elderly. Suggest to him to do his shopping on line and have it delivered to his home. Make sure that he understands that the condition impairs his ability to drive and explain that you have a legal duty to inform the DVLA about his condition. If your patient continues to drive when he is not fit to do so, make every reasonable effort to persuade him to stop.

32 MMI Ethical Dilemma: Disclosure of HIV

Your patient has been having an affair, and he is HIV positive and he doesn't want his wife to know. His wife is also your patient. What would you do?

The big question is whether or not to disclose the diagnosis to his wife.

The GMC (2013) believes that, where HIV infection or AIDS has been diagnosed, any difficulties that arise concerning confidentiality will usually be overcome, if doctors are prepared to discuss openly and honestly with patients the implications of their condition, and the need to protect the safety of others. The GMC has reached the view that there are grounds for such a disclosure only when there is a serious and identifiable risk to specific individuals who, if not so informed, would be exposed to infection.

The wife is also your patient. This creates an immediate dilemma between your duty of confidentiality towards him, and your duty of beneficence towards his wife. Ascertain her level of exposure. Involve the rest of the team for their advice before going ahead. If she is at serious risk of being infected with HIV, encourage the husband to tell his wife he is HIV positive. Remind him of the potential harm to his wife from HIV. He has a legal obligation not to harm her. It may be better for him to reveal the situation to his wife. If he cannot be persuaded, then the risk of harm to his wife would outweigh the risk of harm to the therapeutic relationship, so you are obliged to tell his wife, to protect her health. Refer them both for HIV counselling.

33 MMI Ethical Dilemma: Suspected Child Abuse

You are a junior doctor in casualty, and an 8- year- child comes in with her parents. On examining the child, you notice lots of burn marks which looked like cigarette burns.

What would you do?

Your responsibility is the well-being and safety of the child. Approach the possible diagnosis of child abuse or neglect in the same manner and with the same diligence that you would approach any other disorder. In terms of justice, take into consideration the safety of the child, and your need to protect her. The non-maleficence principle applies. You do not want to falsely accuse a parent of child abuse. It would be devastating for the parent to see their child suffering, and it would be doubly so if they were falsely accused of being the cause. If the child is reluctant to talk in front of the mother, ask the mother to leave the room. With a chaperone, talk with the child about whether something is bothering or hurting her and ask her how the injuries occurred. Ask the parents more details about the incident causing the injury. This may reveal some inconsistencies in their story. If abuse is occurring, other children in the home may also be at risk.

If you are not sure whether or not abuse has occurred, talk to your consultant and ask for a second opinion. If you both feel that she has been abused, contact social services and let them know. Record in detail what you saw and also record your discussions with the parents.

34 MMI Ethical Dilemma: Disclosure of Diagnosis to Second Party

You saw Sarah, who is 21, in your GP surgery five days previously. She had some tests done. You are walking home from the surgery and you meet Sarah's mother. She asks you whether you have her daughter's results yet. What would you do?

It is a breach of confidentiality for you to discuss her daughter. Tell her you cannot discuss any of your patients outside of the surgery. It would be unsafe for you to assume that Sarah does not mind her mother knowing she has visited the doctor.

35 MMI Ethical Dilemma: Suspected Robbery

You are a junior doctor working in A&E. A patient is admitted to A&E with a leg wound. The patient said he tripped and cut his leg. The police arrive and want to interview your patient, whom they suspect was stabbed in the leg whilst committing a robbery. The robber has seriously injured the shopkeeper.

What would you do?

Ask the police what information they have. If your patient fits the description given by the police, check the situation with your team and senior nurse. If you suspect your patient had done an armed robbery and somebody was seriously injured, permit the police to speak to the patient. Inform the patient first. If the police want to see the patient's notes, they must obtain an order from a circuit judge to do so.

36 MMI Ethical Dilemma: Request for IVF from 60 year old

Should a 60- year- old woman be allowed IVF treatment?

There are three important main interests:

- Those of the potential child.
- Those of the 60 year old.
- Those of society more generally.

The interest of the future child is paramount here. A 60- year- old woman has a higher risk of giving birth to a child with genetic disorders. If the child has severe impairments, this will incur considerable cost to the NHS and to society. Because of her age, the woman also has a greater risk of pre-eclampsia, gestational diabetes, and other pregnancy-related problems, which is a cost to society and harm to the mother. The child born to a 60 year- old mother is more likely to lose his mother when he is still very young. This may cause another burden to society. There is a higher risk that a mother who gives birth at 60 may not be able to meet the child's physical, emotional and educational needs as the child gets older. Some people would consider allowing a 60-year-old to have IVF is condoning a form of family life that is not acceptable and is unfair to the child. Even if the woman is paying for the cost of fertility treatment, the issues mentioned above will still have an impact to the NHS and to society generally. On the other hand, should the state interfere in this woman's decision to have a child at 60 years old?

37 MMI Ethical Dilemma: Disclosure of Information to Spouse

You are a junior doctor working in a sexual health clinic. A lady storms into the clinic screaming that she found an appointment belonging to her husband. She demands to know if he has been diagnosed with any infections. Her husband had undergone a full sexual health check-up but the results won't be back for another day.

What would you do?

Take the woman into a private room, which is a safe calm environment, where you can talk. Communicate effectively and sensitively with her. It is vital that you do not breach patient's confidentiality. Be honest and open with her and explain that you cannot break patient confidentiality. In the sexual health clinic doctor/patient confidentiality is an important principle to maintain, as the trust that is formed is vital for the practice of medicine. Patients may need to tell you intimate or embarrassing details about their bodies and lives in order for you to make a diagnosis, and the knowledge that this information will be kept secret will encourage patients to be more forthcoming. Offer her a full sexual health check-up to determine if she has any sexual infections. Explain each test without using any jargon so that she understands clearly what the tests are for. Encourage the husband to discuss the situation with his wife. Suggest making an appointment for relationship counselling.

38 MMI Ethical Dilemma: Can a parent refuse treatment for their child?

Can a parent refuse treatment for their child?

If the parents are refusing consent for the child to receive treatment that the doctor thinks is strongly in the child's best interest, the court will decide whether treatment should be given. Both the parents and doctors are legally obliged to act in the child's best interest. The difficulties arise when there is disagreement. If a 17-year-old with capacity refuses consent for a life and death surgery that the doctors consider on reasonable grounds to be appropriate, then the doctors can proceed with the treatment as long as someone with parental responsibility gives consent. If all those with parental responsibility refuse consent for a procedure that the doctor's think is strongly in the child's best interests, then the doctors should involve the courts. In an emergency, if parental consent is not forthcoming and there is no time to involve the courts, act to save the child from death or serious harm.

What would happen if a child's health is at serious risk, without treatment? For example, in the case of a Jehovah's Witness, if you believe that failure to treat puts the child at significant and unnecessary risk, then you have to give the blood.

39 MMI Ethical Dilemma: Liver Transplant

You have one liver available for transplant and must choose one of two possible patients on the transplant list. One is an ex-alcoholic mother with two young children and the other is a 14- year- old child with congenital liver defect. They both have equal clinical needs.

How would you go about choosing who gets the liver?

This is a very common question asked at interviews.

- You need more information to answer this question. You need a detailed history of each patient.
- They may have other diseases, e.g. cancer, that would affect their life expectancy.
- Who will survive the surgery and its complications?
- Will they be able to take the long term immunotherapy that is required after surgery?
- What is the likely duration of benefit?
- Patients should be treated without judging them.
- Although a patient's illness may have been self-inflicted, we should not discriminate against them.
- For patients on the waiting list, organ allocation is based on the best tissue match and size.
- In situations where two people have an equal match, a points system is used. This looks at impartial factors such as the time on the waiting list, the likelihood of success of treatment, age difference from donor, and is there a match.
- Ex-alcoholics may be in danger of relapse but the girl may have a congenital defect which could damage the new liver.
- Non-judgemental factors such as likelihood of transplant success are particularly useful where the patient's lifestyle may have an impact on a treatment decision e.g. on-going abuse of alcohol may adversely affect the outcome of liver transplantation and the transplant could be denied legitimately on the grounds of futility.
- Discuss the situation with the consultant and the rest of the team.

40 MMI Ethical Dilemma: Organ Donation

What are your views on the Soft Opt-Out for Organ Donation?

England, Scotland, and Wales have moved to the Soft-Opt-Out for Organ Donation.

Everyone **in** England over the age of 18 is considered to be **in** favour of **donating their organs** and tissues after death unless: they have said they don't want to **donate their organs** (they have "opted **out**") People who wish to opt out can do so via an NHS England app. It is anticipated that only those with strong views against organ donation will opt out, thus increasing the number of people who can have transplants and thus fewer people die whilst waiting for a transplant.

The system involves a "soft opt-out", where families could override the presumption in favour of donation if they strongly believed their dead relative would not have wanted it.

Arguments in favour:
- An opt-out system may be promoted by the principles of justice, where more people stand to benefit from a donated organ.
- It would increase the numbers of organs available for transplant.
- Research has shown that the majority of the UK population would be happy to be organ donors after their death.
- When the patient's wishes are unknown, it involves asking the family, at a very difficult and emotional time, for permission to use their organs.
- It does relieve the family of the burden of having to decide.
- It is more cost-effective to maintain a register of the minority, who do not want to donate, rather than the majority, who are willing to be donors.
- Approximately 90% of the population are willing to donate, but only 20% are on the donor register or carry a donor card.
- Nearly 8000 people in the UK are on the transplant waiting list, and every year several hundred patients die while on the list.

Arguments Against:
- An Opt Out system may violate the principle of autonomy, as we should be free to choose what is done to our bodies.
- Failure to withdraw consent may reflect lack of understanding or information rather than agreement with the process.
- Some people with disability and with mental illness may forget that they could opt out if they wanted too.
- Some religious beliefs promote leaving the human body intact after death and relatives may find it distressing that their loved one's body was to be dissected and used.
- Some people feel very uncomfortable donating organs to others, even if these organs are removed after death.

Conclusion: The Opt Out system may be preferable, as it increases the number of organs available, and reduces the number of deaths. The advantages outweigh the disadvantages.

41 MMI Ethical Dilemma: Alternative Cancer Therapy

Your patient has been diagnosed with an aggressive form of cancer. You have advised him to have a course of chemotherapy. He wants to try alternative therapy initially.
What would you say to him?

Autonomy: Adopt an empathetic approach, so that the patient will be able to sense sincere compassion. Form a therapeutic relationship with the patient, so that the patient will feel understood and trusted. The patient has the right to refuse treatment. He needs information about his treatment options and alternatives, in order to make an informed decision. Recommend a course of chemotherapy, but Mr Jones should be the one to decide what treatment he wants.

Beneficence: Act in the best interest of the patient. Honestly express your concerns about the implications of delaying chemotherapy, without downplaying the patient's explicit goal of using alternative therapy with the fewest side effects. Inform him that not using chemotherapy would allow the disease to progress. No clinical trials have been performed to identify the risks and benefits associated with the alternative approach.

Non-maleficence: Mr Jones is a competent person. If there is anger in his response to the diagnosis, recognize this emotion and explore it further. Research the alternative therapies which Mr Jones wants to use, and discuss them with him in a non-judgemental tone. Explore the reasons why Mr Jones does not want chemotherapy. It is a frightening and unpleasant prospect, but perhaps he has been overly influenced by a family member or friend's experience of chemotherapy. Without coercion or manipulation, tell Mr Jones that not using chemotherapy allows the cancer to progress resulting in a massive tumour growth and death. If Mr Jones decides not to have chemotherapy, respect his wishes.

CHAPTER 8

MMI ROLE PLAYING STATION

At the MMI Role Playing Station, you will be asked about many types of scenarios. The interviewer is looking for:

- Honesty and admitting fault, where a mistake was made.
- You always apologise immediately.
- You do not blame anyone else e.g. a member of staff.
- You must take responsibility. By accepting responsibility, you will demonstrate maturity, honesty, and reflection.
- You look for acceptable solutions.
- It is good to compensate in some way i.e. by offering something.
- Try and institute a procedure to ensure it does not happen again.

In order to produce a structured and meaningful answer, you will need to learn to use a number of structures and frameworks that will make your life easier. These will help you to deal with MMI station scenarios involving difficult colleagues, drunk doctors, turning up late etc.

The key interview structure is known as the SEARCH structure. The acronym "SEARCH" stands for
- Seek Information
- Empathy
- Action
- Response
- Consequences
- Harm to patient.

You should use the SEARCH acronym to answer questions on difficult colleagues or conflicts. Over the years, there have seen many questions referring to third year medical students. You must be very careful when you answer these questions because third year students work on hospital wards, and so you must make sure you comment on the implications of them doing so.

For example: You see your friend, a third year medical student, forging a tutor's signature on an attendant sheet. What would do?

As part of your answer, you must comment on the fact that a third year student works on hospital wards and comes into contact with patients. If the student forges signature, perhaps he would forge a signature for prescriptions or drug charts and such like. He could harm patients.

In MMI station questions, the scenario about your friend will vary e.g. the student drinks too much, he forges signature, he cuts corners, he tells lies, etc. These questions are becoming increasingly frequent as it enables interviewers to test your flexibility in dealing with a difficult and sensitive issue.

At the interview, you will be expected to demonstrate that you can handle the situation in a responsible and mature way, ensuring patient safety at all times whilst also resolving the matter sensitively.

The key to success for this type of station is to go in with an open mind and let the troubled friend in this situation tell his/her story.

To ensure that you cover all angles, you will need to consider the following:

Seek Information: Before you jump to conclusions, you need to consider exactly what the facts are.

Empathy: There are reasons for your colleague to behave in this way. His behaviour is likely to have its roots in some kind of personal problems.

Action: What action is needed in this situation? What do you expect your colleague to do and what is expected of you. Have a discussion with him.

Response: If he refuses to go to his tutor and get help, you need to report him to his tutor. If your colleague reports to his tutor and nothing happens, you may need to take further action.

Consequences: Is he aware of the consequences of his actions and what could have happened? How it could affect other medical students, the team, patients, and your colleagues. The incident is likely to have consequences. He must take time off until he gets support.

Harm to Patient: You must assess the situation and make sure at no time is a patient in any harm.

Using the SEARCH structure as a basis for your answer allows you to deal with the above questions by applying the same principles. It also helps you not to forget anything crucial, like harm to a patient.

Examples of 28 Role Play scenarios are set out below and, for ease of reference, they are listed in Annex 2 to this book.

1   **MMI Role Play Station: Dry Cleaning Error**

You are the owner of a dry cleaning business. You have put the wrong dye in the machine and the suit has come out in different colours. The client has arrived to pick up his suit.

What would you say?

- Tell him you have such bad news for him.
- You put the wrong dye in the machine and his suit has an irreparable stain on it.
- Say you are so sorry that this has happened.
- Tell him this has never happened before, and it is totally unacceptable.
- Say he and his family have been coming here for 20 years and you are so proud of your excellent reputation and high standards.
- This is the first time you have had a problem in 20 years.
- Offer two choices to him:
  - You know it is a Marks and Spencers suit and you rang them this morning and they have one in stock. You have given them the measurements and they are holding one for you. They can deliver it here tomorrow morning. You know your customer finishes very late every day so you can drop it around to his flat when he gets home.
  - Or you can give him the money he paid for the suit and he can use it to buy another suit of his choosing.

- As he is one of your best and a long-time customer, you also offer him £50 in vouchers to use the next time he come in.
- Once again you offer sincere apologies.

2 MMI Role Play Station: Request to Forge Signature for a Friend

Your friend is a third year medical student and he has taken up a part time job as he is having financial problems. He has been unable to attend compulsory seminars. Because of his work commitments, he asks you to forge his signature and sign him in.

Seek Information: Meet up with him for an informal chat and a cup of coffee. Find out if not attending classes was a common occurrence. Has he asked other people to forge his signature? Tell him there is a moral dilemma because, on the one hand you have a duty to the University, but, on the other hand you want to help him. Tell him you would not put his name down. Also tell him that it makes you feel uncomfortable to be put in a situation where you feel he is challenging your own sense of morality and involving you with an issue he must deal with.

Empathy: Your friend is going through a difficult time and you would demonstrate concern for him. Give him your time to discuss his problems. Give him your notes if he has already missed some classes.

Action: Advise him to talk to his tutor to see if he can help. Encourage him to go to student services to find out if there is anything they can do to help him financially, so he doesn't have to work so much. Advise him to speak to the medical school, as they are very accommodating in these situations. He would have to speak to his work place and explain his situation and see if they can change his timetable to suit him.

Response: Perhaps by doing the above he will get himself sorted and will be able to attend his classes.

Consequences: Explain to him that it would introduce an injustice to the academic system for other students. He cannot get additional help from the tutor, if he allegedly attended. Highlight the problem of asking you or anyone else to forge his signature. It would have serious consequences for you/anyone else and for him and disciplinary action would probably be taken.

Harm to the patient: If the seminar is compulsory, it is clearly important and if your friend missed it, it would be detrimental to his own knowledge. If he continually missed these important seminars, it could affect his competency as a doctor.

3 MMI Role Play Station: Injured Friend

Your friend, Sarah, is a medical student who is married with two children. Her husband doesn't approve of her studying medicine so she has to study at night. One day she comes into medical school with a black eye.

What would you do?

This is a very typical MMI question and most students forget about the children. In any MMI questions, it is important to always remember if there are children in the scenario. If you do not mention the children you will lose marks.

- The important thing is not to jump to conclusions. Ask her to join you for coffee and have a chat. Encourage her to talk.
- Ask her how she got the black eye, in a direct non-judgemental way. Do not force her if she is not ready to disclose.
- If she told you it was her husband encourage her to tell you about it. Ask if it had happened before and if he had ever hit the children. She might have realistic fears that disclosing the abuse will jeopardize their safety by potentially escalating violence.
- Check if there is an immediate risk to Sarah and her children. If so, what is the extent of the risk? Suggest she takes appropriate measures to ensure her safety and the safety of her children.
- Recommend she goes to her tutor or the social services immediately. The social services are in the crucial position to assist Sarah and to provide her with specialist support services. She might need to go into a safe house with her children.
- She could also discuss it with her GP. Reassure her of her rights to confidentiality.
- If Sarah refuses to get help, you may be justified in disclosing the information to her tutor without her consent, namely where there is a risk of serious harm to Sarah or to her children. Inform Sarah of your intention.
- Reassure Sarah of your ongoing support.

4 MMI Role Play Station: Friend Cheating

You caught your friend, who is a third year medical student, cheating In his exam. OR you are convinced that one of your flat mates, in the year below, has copied a piece of your work and submitted it as her own, knowing that the person who marked your work has left the university.

What would you do?

Seek information: Approach him and ask him what happened today in the exam? Ask him why he cheated and how often has this happened before.

Empathy: If this is your friend's first offence, and may have been brought on by extenuating circumstances that he was unable to deal with, demonstrate concern for him. For example, maybe his mother is dying of cancer and he has problems studying.

Action: Highlight the problem and encourage him to disclose it to his tutor. In the event that this doesn't happen, tell your friend if he refuses, you have a duty to report it. As a member of a profession you are accountable for your own behaviour and for the behaviour of your colleagues.

Response: Hope that he will take responsibility for his actions and tell his tutor. If he has been cheating from the beginning, appropriate disciplinary action will be taken.

Consequences: Tell him that cheating in an exam is blatantly unprofessional. It represents a lack of fairness, lack of integrity and can foreshadow lying in other contexts during his medical training. Not only has he cheated, but he has shown complete disrespect for the medical school and his colleagues.

Harm to the patient: If the student constantly cheats in his exams he will not make a competent doctor. He shows total lack of integrity and he could continue this behaviour on the wards and lie about a lab report etc.

Response: Hope he confesses and that the tutor takes appropriate action.

5   MMI Role Play Station: Finding Syringes at home

You are a third year medical student and you arrive home one evening to find used syringes and needles in the bathroom. Your flatmate is also a third year medical student.

What would you do?

Seek information: Tell him you have seen used needles and syringes in the bathroom and ask him how they got there? If he says they are his, ask him what is happening? If he says he is taking drugs, ask him why he is taking them? Before jumping to conclusions, try and keep an open mind. Listen to his explanation and keep in mind how much pressure your friend is under.

Empathy: There may be several reasons why your friend is taking drugs. He may be depressed or stressed out. There might be something going on in his life that is causing him to take drugs, and you need to know the whole story before jumping to conclusions.

Action: Tell him that he is entering a profession that carries an obligation to its members for self-regulation. As a student, your friend has an opportunity to seek urgent help before serious harm comes to himself, or his patients. He would have to go and see his tutor. He must recognize the duties of a doctor as set out by the GMC 2013. Encourage him to go for counselling. All medical schools offer free counselling for students. If he refuses to tell his tutor, it would be your responsibility to tell the tutor.

Response: The medical school may give him some time off to sort himself out.

Consequences: There is a possibility that his drug taking is affecting his ability to function normally at work and you will need to address this with him. Tell him that being a medical student demands the highest professional standards of any vocation and these expectations dictate that we act with honesty, integrity, and the utmost respect for professionalism.

Harm to patients: As a third year medical student he will be on the wards dealing with patients. Your first priority will be to ensure that patient safety is not compromised. Until he gets himself sorted, he cannot go on the wards, and he would be unable to practice medicine with reasonable skill and safety. He could steal drugs and syringes from the ward, and he could even steal money from patients to buy the drugs. Impaired students become impaired doctors.

6 MMI Role Play Station: Overdose

If a patient comes into casualty after taking an overdose of paracetamol, and he wants to discharge himself, what would you say to him?

Explain to the patient that he has taken an overdose of approximately 50 tablets and this could cause serious liver damage and renal failure.
- Tell him you have sent his blood away for analysis, and that you might have to do a gastric washout and explain the reason for the washout.
- Put up an intravenous drip and give him some drugs to reduce liver damage.
- Paracetamol starts to take effect after a few hours, so he needs to be closely monitored for the next 24 hours to make sure that he is safe from the lethal effect of the drug.
- From his notes you see this is his third overdose, so you need to refer him to a psychiatrist to see why he wants to take his own life.
- Advise him of all the reasons why it would be in his best interest to stay in hospital.
- Always act in his best interest and therefore make sure that before he leaves the hospital, he is safe from the lethal effects of the paracetamol.

7 MMI Role play Station: Sharing Library Card

As a third year medical student you have signed an agreement that allows you to use a library card that grants you access to the hospital library. Access is restricted to doctors and medical students who are currently based at the hospital. Your close friend, from your old school, wishes to use the library to revise for her exams as it is quieter than the school library, and she asks to use your card for the day.

How will you deal with this situation?
Which ethical issues does this scenario raise?
Can the candidate consider more than one perspective?
What difficulties may arise?
How important are communication skills in such a scenario?

8 MMI Role Play Station: Classmate Skipping Classes

Your friend Mary has not come to class for a few days. She is usually hard-working and she very seldom skips classes.

What would you do?

- Find a quiet, private place to talk to Mary. You may find that Mary is depressed and drunk. If you ask the right questions, she may tell you that she is suicidal. Unlike the dilemma-type questions, which are designed to reveal your problem solving and reasoning skills, the acting stations are there to test your ability to respond to physical and verbal cues, and to communicate under stressful situations etc. Use your empathy skills.
- Encourage her to talk and listen to her trials and tribulations. She might be finding it all too stressful, she might have family problems, or just has difficulties settling into medical school.
- If you think she is depressed, encourage her to go for counselling. Reassure her about the confidentiality of the counselling services, and offer to go with her. Encourage her to talk to her tutor.
- If you feel that Mary is a danger to herself or to others, and does not want to address the situation, then you have no option but to discuss the matter with her tutor.
- Give her support through this difficult time.

9 MMI Role Play Station: Weight Problem

Mary comes to see you in your clinic. She is struggling with her weight problem. She feels frustrated and disrespected by the previous doctor.

What would you do?

Explain that, because she is overweight, she faces the potential health problems that arise from obesity e.g. liver disease, diabetes, coronary artery disease, high blood pressure and musculoskeletal problems. The best way to solve these problems is for the patient to change her habits: eat less, exercise more.

She has tried this and not succeeded. Agree with Mary that the task is a difficult one, but re-emphasise its importance. Have a non-judgemental, compassionate attitude to help establish patient's trust.

Refer Mary to a dietician, a psychologist and a physiotherapist to devise a more structured programme. Make sure that she understands the risks of her current condition, and the preferred approach to minimize those risks. Explain to the patient that each of her conditions will improve with weight loss.

Patient motivation for making difficult behavioural changes is a complex phenomenon that requires sensitivity, flexibility, and persistence on the part of the doctor. The potency of small improvements can be increased by emphasizing more subjective measures, such as how the patient will feel after weight loss, e.g. more energy, reduced fatigue, greater mobility and ability to enjoy themselves.

Establish initially modest expectations, provide consistent feedback, monitor adherence, and offer constructive encouragement. Observe carefully the patient's words and non-verbal cues, and respond appropriately. Acknowledge her life experiences and knowledge of her body, enquire about and listen to her emotional experiences, including the degree to which she feels frustrated and disrespected by the previous doctor.

If her obesity persists, in spite of on-going attempts at behavioural modifications, Mary may become a candidate for bariatric surgery.

10 MMI Role Play Station: Forging Signature

Your friend is a third year medical student. He went to bed drunk at 4am and woke up with a terrible hangover and couldn't get out of bed next morning to attend his compulsory lecture. Rather than get into trouble he forged his tutor's signature in his log-book.

What would you do?

Seek information: Find a quiet place and ask your friend what happened to him this morning and why did he forge the tutor's signature? Try to determine if this was out of character for him or had he done this several times.

Empathy: Be non-judgemental towards him. Everyone has difficulties from time to time. He may have problems with time management and is feeling overwhelmed by the whole course. Show your support by offering him the time to discuss his problems.

Action: Advise him to speak to his tutor and confess what he has done. Also tell him if he refuses, you will have to tell the tutor. Remaining silent about him having forged his tutor's signature, may allow your friend to get through medical school with significant gaps in his knowledge, and will not make him a competent doctor. Encourage him to go for counselling.

Consequences: Remind him the doctor's role in society is one who is reliable and trustworthy and forging the tutor's signature was not acceptable and such behaviour as a doctor could have consequences not only for himself, but for the patients. Explain the gravity of his offence, and that forging is both criminal and deceitful.

Response: Each of us has a responsibility to ensure that the code of professional conduct is adhered to by all students.

Harm to patient: Inadequate knowledge may mean patients in the future are at risk from the student's lack of experience. Think of the criminal repercussions of forging a signature on a prescription for example.

11 MMI Role Play Station: Prescription with Allergic Reaction

You are a consultant and your junior doctor gave a patient ear-drops which contain pea nut oil, and the patient has an allergy to peanuts. She was very ill and ended up in casualty. She comes to see you next day and she is very upset.

What would you do?

- Introduce yourself and apologise on behalf of Dr Brown, the junior doctor.
- Make sure the patient feels listened to and respected.
- Check how the patient is feeling now.
- Explain what is likely to happen now in terms of symptoms and the best treatment.
- Tell the patient that her notes state that she has an allergy to peanut oil, and Dr Brown should not have prescribed peanut oil.
- Be open and honest with the patient. Explain fully and promptly what has happened.
- Put matters right by changing her medication.
- Tell her that you had a meeting with Dr Brown and discussed the

incident at the practice this morning with all the staff, to make sure this does not happen again, either to her or to any other patient.

- Something as serious as a patient allergy should not have been missed and, from now on, you will have a card inside all patients notes, on the front page specifically for allergies.
- If she wanted to take the complaint further, give her the details of PALS.
- GMC's Good Medical Practice 2006 p31 states: Doctors should provide patients who complain with a prompt, open, constructive and honest response including an explanation and, if appropriate, an apology.
- Patients who complain generally want an explanation of what happened, an apology, and reassurance that it will not happen again.
- Patients who have made a complaint also want to know that lessons will be learnt. It is important that doctors are fully aware of and trained in the complaints procedure.

12 MMI Role Play Station: Drunk Student

Your friend, who is a third year medical student, is drinking alcohol at lunchtime and going on the wards.

What would you do?

Seek information: Wait until he is on his own and ask him to join you for coffee. The key to success for this type of station is to go in with an open mind and let the troubled friend, in this situation, tell his story. Tell him you noticed he is often very tired lately. Ask him if he is stressed or is there any reason why he started drinking at lunchtimes. Some people might start on the wrong foot and begin to lecture him too early. For example, telling him he shouldn't be drinking so much. You must suspend your judgement and focus on helping your friend. Invite him to share the reason why he is drinking at lunch-time. On the surface, he may be a party-goer, who risks patient safety and his personal safety. When questioned, he may provide irresponsible answers such as: "I just like to get drunk and I can perform in the hospital just fine even if I have a few drinks". He may even get defensive: "What do you care?" Upon persistence and non-judgemental questioning, he may reveal that he is under a lot of pressure and finding it extremely difficult to cope. He may not be sure if medicine is for him. Lots of stress results from the internal conflict, and he escapes by going to parties, drinking at lunchtime, and forgetting about his worries.

Empathy: This requires an empathetic approach. Watch out for your friend's posture, emotions, keywords like: 'drinking takes away my problems'. Listening skills are very important here.

Action: Highlight the problem and encourage him to disclose it to his tutor immediately. In the event that he refuses, you would have to take action and tell his tutor. Let him know that, just because nothing bad happened on the wards this afternoon, this does not mean that he can exonerate himself from responsibility. Tell him that you cannot be a silent bystander observing a series of actions, by him, that you consider as inappropriate, unprofessional and reckless. Encourage him to reflect on what brought him into medicine in the first place. Advise him to seek help immediately. Each medical school has a free counselling service. Reassure him about the confidentiality of the counselling service and encourage him to seek proper help. Explain to him it is better to address the problem at an early stage than let it develop into a huge problem. Acknowledge how well he did in his first three years and help him recognize the progress he has made. Tell him he deserves credit and respect for his dedication and perseverance up to now. By getting help he can overcome his hurdles and get back on track.

Response: Hope that he will go to see his tutor and have counselling. He will not be able to go on the wards until he has sorted himself out and is aware of the consequences of his actions.

Consequences: Let him know that turning up on the ward smelling of alcohol shows a serious lack of judgement that could have a devastating impact on patients. He should recognize the duties of a doctor as set out by the GMC 2013.

Harm to patient: Because of his drinking, patient care could have been in serious jeopardy. The GMC states in Tomorrow's Doctors: 'Students must be aware that their behaviour outside the clinical environment, including in their personal lives, may have an impact on their fitness to practice. Their behaviour at all times must justify the trust the public places in the medical profession; misconduct includes issues that raise a question about a doctor's probity, trustworthiness or character".

In any of these situations you must be aware of the following:
- Show empathy and demonstrate concern.
- Recognise that this shows a lack of judgement and integrity.

- Recognise the duties of a doctor as set out by the GMC 2013.
- Always discuss the issue with the individual first before reporting him to his tutor.
- Encourage him to go to his tutor and seek help.
- Tell the tutor, if he refuses.
- If he is a third year medical student, he will be on the wards looking after patients.
- Patient safety is paramount.

13 MMI Role Play Station: Consultant Smelling of Alcohol

You are a junior doctor and one of the consultants comes into the ward smelling of alcohol?

What would you do?

Seek information: Try to clarify if the alcohol was from the night before or if he had been drinking that morning. Regardless, your first priority will be to ensure that patient safety is not compromised. Integrity, responsibility and ensuring the safety of the patients are critical for a doctor.

Empathy: A certain level of tact is required. There may be several reasons behind the consultant's behaviour. He may be depressed, stressed out or he may have personal problems. You must have a non-judgemental approach towards him.

Action: Involve another senior member of the team or the ward manager. Make sure the matter is dealt with sensitively, without the knowledge of his patients, and with as little embarrassment as possible. Ensure that the consultant stops working and goes home by taxi. All the patients he had seen that morning have to be reviewed by another consultant. If the consultant was due to operate that afternoon, his senior colleagues would involve other doctors to make sure the team can cope.

Response: The consultant would have to take time off to sort himself out. He needs to go for counselling. You do not gossip about this issue.

Consequences: Many critical management decisions are made during ward rounds. Any patient would be outraged if he or she were to find out that the consultant smelled of alcohol or had consumed alcohol. What would happen if the alcohol had caused the doctor to forget a small but crucial detail, and that had led to a larger catastrophe?

Harm to patient: The consultant coming in to work smelling of alcohol could have a devastating effect on patients. Alcohol impairs judgement and slows reaction time. It would clearly place him at a clinical disadvantage and might result in significant adverse consequences.

14 MMI Role Play Station: Fear of Flying

Helen had a friend who was killed in the plane crash on 9/11. She is due to fly to Manchester for an urgent business meeting with you. This is her first time flying since her friend died. She is petrified. You are at the airport and Helen has just arrived. She is in an incapacitating amount of fear and experiencing a high level of anxiety.

This is a good example of a communication skills station.
- Be supportive and understand that her fears are very real and significant to her.
- Listen to her fears and try and understand what she is going through.
- Adjust communication to suit the situation. Even though her fear appears unwarranted or exaggerated to others, the fear is real to her and should not be dismissed.
- Try and make her feel at ease. Do not expect Helen to snap out of it or to get over it in a matter of minutes. That response is insensitive and unrealistic.
- Attempt to understand Helen's point of view.
- Avoid making light of Helen's concern.
- Normalise concerns. Many other normal people have similar fears. Tell her that these feelings of anxiety are common.
- Confirm, without being patronizing, that Helen is aware of the relative safety of air travel. There is better security now in place at the airport, there are many cameras everywhere, and there is statistically little chance of being targeted etc.
- Help Helen arrive at a reasonable course of action, perhaps by separating her intellectual response of low danger from the emotional response of anxiety.
- It is very important not to offer inappropriate reassurance. Do not say you know what she is going through, because you do not.

- Recommend that she joins support groups where she can talk to other people facing similar problems so she won't feel alone, and have a social support group while she works to overcome her fear of flying.

15 MMI Role Play: Team Member not Pulling his Weight

You have been working in a group project over the last 3 months with 5 other people. One of the students doesn't show up for meetings and, when he does, he shows up late and leaves early. He has put no effort into the group project but shows up on the day of the presentation and tries to take credit for the project.

What would you do?

- It is a bit too late to wait until the day of the presentation. He has not been pulling his weight for three months. If the rest of the group did not say anything to him for the last three months, it is too late to get upset on the last day when the inevitable happens.
- As no one told him, he is entitled to share the group mark.
- In this situation, speak to the team member directly on your own, in the first week.
- Approach the conversation with an open mind and in a non-judgemental manner.
- It is entirely possible that this person has a legitimate reason for not pulling his weight in the group.
- Ask him if he is enjoying the group and how he thinks he is working in the group.
- If he acknowledges that he had not been contributing as much as he should be, appreciate his honesty.
- If he had a legitimate reason for this, e.g. feeling stressed out, having family issues, offer him your support.
- Do whatever you can to help him, especially if he is having difficulties coping.
- This could mean spending more time with him discussing ideas or helping him to manage his time better.
- Re-arrange the meeting times so he can arrive on time and leave at the same time as everyone else.
- If he did not want to contribute to the group, or thought he was contributing enough, encourage him to reconsider his involvement for both his own and mutual benefit.

- Explain that he can learn a lot from the group work and everyone else in the group can learn a lot from his ideas.
- It is in everyone's best interest if he is an active member of the group.
- If he is just lazy, discuss the situation with the rest of the group and come to a decision together.
- Meet up with him and tell him that this situation cannot continue. If he is not prepared to pull his weight, he has to leave the group and make other arrangements.

16 MMI Role Play: Speaking to a Patient with Epilepsy

You are a junior doctor. Your patient is diagnosed with severe epilepsy. He is a driving instructor. You have to tell him that he cannot drive. His wife has depression, he has a child, and he is the sole earner.

You will be tested on your attitude, body language and whether or not you develop a rapport with the patient. If the patient gets angry, do not interrupt him. Allow him to vent his anger.

Do not say you understand how they feel, because you don't. You can say you can see why he feels that way. Allow the patient to interupt you. Encourage him to do so at any time as you speak.

Use a soft tone of voice, and speak slowly and clearly. Pause to let the patient take in what you are saying. Summarise what you have said, to make sure the patient fully understands.

Offer direction to other sources of help.

The following are useful ways to communicate in an empathetic manner: It's the first time I have seen you.

Can we start from the beginning?

Can you tell me, in your own words, what has been happening?

Have you ever had a fit before? Did anyone witnessed that?

I see you are a driving instructor. Your wife does not work, and you have a daughter. That must be quite stressful on you now that you are the sole breadwinner.

Do you have any ideas about the cause of your seizures?

Is there anything in particular you are concerned about? What were you hoping I could do for you today?

What have you been told so far?

What do you know about seizures, and driving?

Do you realise that, whilst driving, you could have a seizure and endanger your life, the life of your students, or the life of the general public?

I am afraid I have some bad news for you. Based on your results, I am certain you have had a seizure, and you have Epilepsy.

What does this mean for me? It means you cannot drive for six months. I am sorry this is not better news.

What can we do about it? You can speak to an employer about a role that doesn't involve driving. I can write a sick note/letter of support to your employer. This must be very difficult: not being able to carry on as a driving instructor, and your concern about not being able to provide for your family.

Have you spoken to the DVLA?

If his wife is involved, ask her if she has any thoughts about what may persuade him? Has he had any other funny turns? What medication is he taking? Explain that he would be putting himself and others at risk. We need to think about the best things to do today.

This must be frustrating but legally you cannot drive. What happens next? You must inform DVLA and your car insurance company.

I don't want to do that. Unfortunately, if you don't inform them, I have a professional duty to do so.

Emotion: I can see you are quite upset. It's ok for you to be upset. I can see this is upsetting news for you. I wish the news were better.

Summary: Anything unclear? Anything else you want to ask? I would like to see you again in a few weeks. If you have any problems with your employer, please let me know.

When dealing with emotional situations, consider the following four factors:

Physical Social Psychological Financial
- For example:
  If a patient is depressed and you have to chat with her, consider the following:

Physical
- How long have you been feeling depressed?
- How does the depression affect your daily life?
- How are you sleeping at night?
- Are you on any medication?
- Are you experiencing any side affects?

Social
- Tell me about yourself.
- Tell me about your home life.
- Tell me about your family.
- Is there anyone you can talk to?
- Do you have friends to go out with?
- Do you drink or smoke?
- Are you concerned about how much you are drinking?

Psychological
- How long have you been feeling depressed?
- How is your depression affecting your daily life?
- How are you coping?
- You said you were worried about the children. Why?
- How do you manage with the children?
- What is your daily routine?
- Do you manage to go out at night and meet with your friends?
- What sort of things are you having difficulty coping with?
- Have you considered getting any help? For example, counseling.
- Is there anything you would like me to do?
- What do you see as the best way forward?

Financial

- What sort of financial support is she having?
- What sort of work is she doing?
- How does her depression affect her work?
- How does she manage to take drugs, and survive at work?

General Tips

- Make sure the setting is right.
- You might want to move the chairs so that you are sitting closer to each other.
- Encourage them to talk, by asking lots of open questions. For example: Tell me what is happening for you?
- Let them talk and express their feelings.
- If the patient expresses an emotion, it should be acknowledged and further explored.
- Don't interrupt and ask questions; give them time.
- This requires an empathetic approach.
- Listening skills are very important.
- Encourage them to talk, and listen to their trials and tribulations.
- Don't offer your opinions.
- Maintain good eye contact.
- Don't be judgmental.
- Your tone of voice is extremely important. Use appropriate facial expressions.
- Don't give advice.
- Don't be afraid of silence.
- Nodding, hand gestures, and "Hmm" are very important.
- You may be faced with a grieving patient: Stay calm. Give them time. Do not rush to stop them crying.
- "I can see you are very upset. That's quite understandable, given what's happened".
- Concentrate on the patient's feelings at this moment. Do not assume you know how they are feeling.
- "Would you like a tissue or a drink"?
- Do not tell them to stay calm, or not to worry, or that everything will be ok.
- Do not offer inappropriate reassurance. Do not say: "I know what you are going through" because you don't.

Dealing with an angry person in the role play.

- The 'angry patient' is a common scenario in the MMI because it's such a common scenario in medicine. Patients can be angry for many reasons: stress of the illness, dealing with the unknown, powerless, afraid, feeling they are not being heard, etc.
- If you are dealing with an angry person, keep calm and allow him to vent his anger. Acknowledge the person's feelings: 'I can see you are really upset and angry '
- 'What can I do to stop you feeling so angry?' Try to understand why he is so angry. 'Can you tell me what happened?' 'Let me see if I have understood the situation. You don't feel the nurses are listening to you. You are in a lot of pain, and the current pain medications are not working for you.
- 'I am sorry you are in such pain. I will talk to the team now, and see if we can write you up for a stronger pain killer. Before I take care of that, I want to see if there is anything else I can do for you?'
- 'I am sorry you feel so angry about this.' 'I am really sorry you have to go through all this.'
- It is important that the patient feels they have been heard. Apologising to the patient does not mean you have accepted responsibility, if you did nothing wrong. You are apologising to the patient for what he is going through.
- Be aware of your non-verbal behavior: good eye contact, head nodding, forward lean, and more direct body orientation, with uncrossed arms and legs, to show you are active listening to the patient.
- Explore any other solutions.
- Do you have some suggestions on ways to solve the problem? If the doctor is running late and the patient is angry: 'I am so sorry for keeping you waiting so long. Unfortunately, I cannot predict when there is going to be an emergency. This morning, one of my patients had a heart attack and it took up some time to care for her. That's what made me so late for your appointment. I do apologise for keeping you waiting for so long. Your time is precious, and important to me. I hope you understand.'
- It may be that he has legitimate concerns or has misunderstood the situation. Good communication is needed. Listen, negotiate and compromise to reach resolution. Adopt a soft approach, and try and gain his trust.

17 MMI Role Play Station: Colleague faking Illness

Your colleague, who is a junior doctor, has called in sick. You cannot provide cover as you have already made plans. Later that evening, your colleague, who has called in sick, is at the same party you are attending.

What would you do?

- Approach my colleague at an appropriate time during the evening. Allow him the chance to explain himself.
- If he had no reason for doing this, tell him that it is unethical and that he is letting down himself and the team.
- Discuss the situation with the rest of the team.

18 MMI Role Play Station: Patient given wrong Vaccine

You are a GP and one of your patients received the wrong type of vaccine. What would you do?

- Apologise to the patient and provide them with a clear explanation of how it happened.
- Take steps to deal with the consequences and arrange appropriate treatment and follow up.
- Speak to the individual who made the mistake. Arrange a meeting to discuss it with all the staff.
- This error would be considered as an adverse incident, for the practice to review and consider any lessons that can be learned.
- Record all the information in the patient's notes. This is invaluable evidence in the event of a complaint.
- Also, update the patient about the changes made to practice procedures to prevent a repeat of what has occurred. It will let him know that you are taking the mistake very seriously.

19 MMI Role Play Station: Issuing Doctor's Note

You are a GP. One of your patients, Tom, did not attend one of his classes and missed an important exam. He told you that his teacher would like a doctor's note explaining his absence from class: otherwise, he will fail. He wants you to write a note for him, indicating that he was not feeling well enough to sit the exam.

What are the issues here?

- Examine him and consider all the facts. If you find that he is not ill, do not give him a sick note.
- A sick note is a legal document and you would not act against your best judgement.
- The GMC's Good Medical Practice clearly states: 'you must do your best to make sure that any documents you write or sign are not false or misleading'.
- Honesty and professional integrity are very important and in this case the public's trust in the profession is being jeopardised.
- Tell Tom that you cannot give him a note for non–medical reasons. Explain to him that you cannot verify that he was unwell at that time.

20 MMI Role Play: How would you deal with an angry patient?

The patient's surgery has been cancelled for three days in a row. The patient may be angry for many reasons. The patient may be frightened, confused or lonely. She might be on medication that alters her mood.

Good communication is needed. Listen, negotiate and compromise to reach resolution.
- Speak to the patient in a private room and turn off your bleeper to ensure that you are not disturbed.
- Listen to what the patient is saying, her concerns, and her expectations.
- It may be that the patient has legitimate concerns or has misunderstood the situation.
- Remain calm and allow the patient to vent her anger.
- Acknowledge the patient's feelings e.g. tell her you can see that she is very upset and angry.
- Have an empathetic approach towards the patient. Offer an apology and explain fully and promptly to the patient what has happened. You are sorry that her operation has been cancelled but you had several emergencies, due to an accident on the motorway, which took priority.
- Negotiate a compromise and check if there are any cancellations for tomorrow, and fit her in, if that suited her?
- Ask the patient if she has any questions.
- Offer further support and let her know you will get back to her later that day. Do not promise anything that you cannot deliver on.

21 Role Play Station: Mistake with a Cake

You have been asked by a lady to prepare a cake for her daughter's wedding. The lady made it clear that the cake had to be gluten or nut free; however, you forgot to note this down when you took the order. On the day of the wedding, the lady arrives to collect the cake.

How do you deal with the situation?

.

This is a similar role play to the lady in the launderette (number 1).

- Be honest and admit the fault.
- Always apologise immediately.
- Do not blame anyone else, like a member of staff
- Take responsibility. By accepting responsibility, you will demonstrate maturity, honesty, and reflection.
- Look for acceptable solutions.
- Tell her you are really sorry. You did not write down that two of the children needed gluten/nut free cake.
- It is totally your fault. You have two choices for her. You are aware that the reception is not until 5 p.m. which gives you plenty of time to bake a new cake. Or you can make, for the two children, a special small cake identical to the big cake, which is gluten/nut free.
- You will not be charging her for either of the cakes.
- You will take the cakes in person to the reception at 5 p.m.
- Ask her what she would prefer, and again offer your sincere apologies.

22 MMI Role Play Station: Colleague Consistently Late

You are a junior doctor and one of your colleagues consistently arrives late for his shifts

What would you do?

- The most appropriate step, in the first instance, is to discuss the situation directly with the doctor concerned.
- This may then lead to an admission by your colleague that there is a problem at home and he may then seek appropriate help.
- Offer your support. If he denies there is a problem, you would have an obligation to take the matter further and to speak to the consultant, as this may affect patient safety.

- If he is turning up late, it may have a negative impact on your own workload.
- If your other colleagues have been affected by his lateness, you might need to discuss the matter with them.
- The GMC advises that your duty is to put patients' interests first and to act to protect them, and must override personal and professional loyalties.

23 MMI Role Play Station: Colleague with Cocaine Addiction

One of your colleagues confides in you that he has a cocaine addiction problem. He is asking you to keep the information to yourself.

What would you do?
- The care of his patients is your primary concern.
- The GMC advises that, as a doctor, your primary duty is to your patients. If you feel that patient safety is at risk due to a colleague's conduct, performance or health, then you have an obligation to take steps to protect them.
- Tell your colleague that you will support him, but tell him that he needs to address the matter with his consultant.
- If he refuses to do so, you have no option but to report him.
- Keep a record of your conversation with him. Recommend that he goes for counselling and takes time off to solve his addiction.
- His addiction is likely to have its roots in some kind of personal problems.
- Show as much support as you can towards him.
- If he is taking time off, the team will have to function properly without him. You need to be flexible and adaptable.
- You need to ensure that patient care is covered adequately whilst his addiction is being resolved.

24 MMI Role Play Station: Social Networking Sites

Your friend is a junior doctor and you notice that your friend has posted photographs of himself on a social networking site, where he is shown drinking heavily, vomiting and looking dreadful at 4 a.m.

What would you do about it?

- Arrange to meet your friend.
- Tell him to take the pictures down immediately.
- Explain to him that his behaviour is unprofessional.
- Let him know that he is placing a burden on his colleagues, and risks compromising his own career, and that of the medical professional.
- Check with him if this was the first time or is it a regular event.
- Check if he is having problems and if he needs some help.

25 MMI Role Play Station: Drunk Patient

You are the doctor in Casualty and there is a four-hour wait to be seen. A drunk patient begins shouting and threating staff because he wants to be seen immediately.

What would you do?

- Try to calm down the patient by talking to him and explaining that you are there to help him.
- Adopt a soft approach and try and gain his trust.
- Apologise to the patient for the long wait.
- Explain to him that it is extremely busy and you have to prioritise, and firstly treat the patients who are severely ill and coming in by ambulance.
- In dealing with difficult patients, take into consideration why they are in casualty. He may be in a lot of pain.
- Being drunk may cloak a dangerous illness.
- He may be having a hypoglycaemic attack.
- Tell the patient that you had not forgotten him and he will be called when it is his turn.
- If he carries on been abusive, ask him to remain quiet and wait his turn.
- Call security to keep an eye on him.
- Never allow a difficult patient to jump the queue because of his threats, as this would be unfair to the other patients.

26 MMI Role Play Station: Complaint about Standard of Care

You are the doctor on the medical ward. A patient's relative stops you in the corridor, mentioning that she is upset with the standard of care on the ward.

What would you do?

- Find a quiet room and discuss with the relative what her concerns are.
- If you cannot deal with the complaint, refer her to someone who can deal with it.
- If there are nursing concerns, refer her to the ward manager. Tell the ward manager what is happening.
- If the concerns are clinical, refer her to the consultant.
- It is important that the relative feels she is being listened to.
- It is important to diffuse problems before they escalate into a formal complaint.
- If she still is not satisfied that the complaint is dealt with properly, give her the phone numbers of PALS (Patient Advice and Liaison Service) and inform her how PALS can help her.

27 MMI Role Play Station: Accidental Needle Injury to Self

You are a junior doctor assisting the consultant with an operation. Just when the consultant was suturing the patient his bleeper goes and he is called away in an emergency. He asks you to finish suturing the patient. While suturing, you accidently prick your finger. You are worried that you may be at risk of contracting a blood-borne disease.

What would you do?

- Check the hospital policies and guidelines on what you should do in these specific circumstances.
- Inform the consultant and the rest of the team.
- Try to ascertain the patient's previous clinical history, to determine what you may be exposed to.
- If the occupational health department is closed, go to Casualty to see if you can get a Hepatitis B Booster vaccination.
- Try not to get involved in the process.
- It is be more appropriate to get another doctor from the team to take the patient's bloods.
- Your team should explain to the patient what has happened.
- The team would take a sample of the patient's blood, with his consent, to send off for testing for HIV and any other blood-borne diseases.
- Let Occupational Health know as soon as possible so that they can document the incident and can arrange for further testing.
- Book some counselling sessions.

28 MMI Role Play Station: Request from Colleague for Prescription

You are a junior doctor on the medical ward. Your colleague is planning to travel for three months and he has forgotten to get anti-malarial medication. He asks you to prescribe some anti-malarial medication for him to take on his travels.

What would you do?

- Recommend that he goes to see his GP, as his GP has his medical history and can prescribe the right medication.
- The GMC (2013) states clearly that doctors should avoid treating themselves or those close to them.

29 MMI Role Play Station: Suspect Colleague Possesses Cocaine

You are working as a junior doctor and you are in the canteen having lunch with your colleague. You notice that what looks like a packet of cocaine has fallen out of his bag.

What are the issues here?

- As a doctor, patient safety is always your first priority.
- Ask your colleague what is in the bag. If he tells you it is cocaine, ask him why he has cocaine in his pocket?
- At this stage, you have no reason to believe that patient care is being jeopardised.
- Have a chat with your colleague and offer him appropriate emotional support and clarify the situation.
- This may then lead to an admission by your colleague that there is a problem.
- Recommend that he receive appropriate help as soon as possible.
- If he denies there is a problem, and pretends that someone planted the packet in his pocket, you have an obligation to take the matter further and speak to his consultant.
- If he accepts the drugs are his and he refuses to seek help, discuss the incident with the consultant.

30 MMI Role Play Station: Collaboration Station

This is now common in some MMI stations. Before entering the station, the student reads instructions on how to assemble a complex model, for example. In the station, he then gives verbal only instructions to another person (sometimes another applicant or a member of staff) who has to complete the task. These stations are used to test your teamwork, problem solving, and communication skills. Sometimes they have Lego or building blocks.

Read the instructions carefully. Break down the task into small steps, and give clear concise instructions for each step of the task. Ask them to let you know if anything is not clear, or if they have not understood the instruction. Tell them to feel free to interrupt you anytime. If a mistake is made, immediately tell them, but stay calm and give encouragement throughout, and show empathy.

CHAPTER 9

MMI PERSONAL SKILLS STATIONS

Medical schools are looking for well-rounded, sociable people who will contribute positively to medical school life. Extra-curricular activities demonstrate these qualities and show that you have good team-working, leadership and communication skills. **In this Chapter, there are 44 examples (which are listed in Annex 3), and how to answer these questions.**

1 MMI Personal Skills: Leadership

What are the qualities of a good leader?

- Has clear objectives and communicates them effectively to the team so they can take responsibility to achieve their own goals.
- Delegate tasks to team members who have the right skill set. Must know the strength, weakness and aspiration of each team member.
- Motivates and encourages the team to give 100%.
- Will use a variety of styles of leadership according to the situation and the individuals involved.
- Provides a supportive environment and encourages learning and personal development.
- Praises and encourages each member of the team. Supports members who are in need of help. Reward good performance.
- Is consistent and fair towards all.
- Has initiative and resilience to cope with setbacks and adapt to rapidly changing circumstances.
- Able to build rapport, listen, persuade, negotiate and give constructive criticism
- Is visionary in outlook, has the courage to reappraise situations and decisions.
- Welcomes challenges and respect criticisms.
- Takes responsibility for mistakes.

- Removes obstacles to achieve group goals.
- Deals with problems immediately before they escalate.
- Ensures greater collaboration and achieves common goals.
- Negotiates and influences others, building consensus and gaining cooperation from others.
- Puts good mechanisms in place to resolve conflicts constructively.

2 MMI Personal Skills: Team Player

What are the qualities of a good team player?

- Communicates constructively.
- Keeps the team up to date about progress.
- Listens carefully to the views of others.
- Has initiative and resilience to cope with setbacks and adapts to rapidly changing circumstances.
- Is enthusiastic and motivated.
- Takes responsibility for one's own work and achieves the results that are required of him.
- Shares ideas and discusses areas to resolve problems.
- Takes responsibility and ownership for his role.
- Accepts and learns from constructive criticism.
- Has ability to work effectively in different teams.
- Welcomes feedback, knows when to seek help from others.
- Is flexible and adaptable. Is willing to change his own views and compromise to get a group decision.

3 MMI Personal Skills: Personal Description

How would your friends describe you?
Name three adjectives that you think best suit you?

Suggested responses:

- My friends would describe me as kind, a good listener, with a good sense of humour.
- As captain of my hockey team, my teammates would say I am flexible and a fair team leader.
- When I did a charity walk for my school with a group of my friends, they said I am hardworking, motivated and good at multitasking.

Medicine is all about team work. Medical schools want to see some evidence that you can work effectively in a team. When you describe yourself, explain what part of the team were you in, what and how did you contribute, what were the problems you encountered, what did you achieve?

- Are you more of a player or a leader?
- Never say you were never a leader or never a player.
- It is always best to say you are a bit of both.

4   MMI Personal Skills: What are your strengths/weaknesses?

Be able to describe how your strengths add to the contributions you make to the teams in which you play, as team player and team leader. When asked what are your strengths and weaknesses, always start off with your strengths. Give about 10 of your strengths and about 1-2 weaknesses.

Examples of strengths:

- I am conscientious, hardworking and motivated and as a result I have got very high grades in my GCSE, A levels and music exams.
- I am a very caring, empathetic person with good listening skills.
- When I did some work experience in my local hospital a 35-year-old woman, with three young children, was told she had six months to live. I spent a lot of time listening to all her concerns. I put myself in her shoes and really felt how difficult her situation was. She told the doctor that I made a real difference to her, by letting her get it all off her chest.
- I have worked as both a team player and leader. As a team leader, I had to organize a charity-do for my local hospice.
- Being approachable, flexible, and a good communicator helped me to make the event very successful.
- I am very organized and I have a lot of experience at multitasking.
- During the past few years, I have studied for my A levels and music exams, worked at weekends in my local hospice, played in the orchestra, and organized a charity event. I used my diary to make sure everything ran smoothly.
- I am conscientious and hardworking and as a result I consistently achieve high grades at school.
- Another one of my strengths is my communication skills. I am regarded by my friends as someone who is approachable, reliable with a good sense of humour.

- I had the opportunity to test my listening and empathy skills at the local hospice when one of my patients had Alzheimer's. Her daughter was very upset that her mother recognized her and an hour later the mother had no idea who the daughter was. She was very upset and I sat with her and listened to her frustrations and allowed her to let it all out.
- I am also a keen sports person who understands the importance of team work. I have enhanced my leader ship skills by setting up various projects etc. I hope to continue my passion for rugby when I am at medical school. I find competitive sports keep me focused and motivated. This contributed greatly to my studies, in helping me appreciate the impact of good teamwork and good communication.
- Sports also help me to push myself to the limit. At times, as a medical student, you have to push yourself to the limit. Sports keep me focused and I do not give up easily.

Weaknesses:

This is one of the toughest questions asked by medical schools. Last year, several medical schools asked students to give them five of their weaknesses.

- Do not sit there giving them five of your weaknesses. Just give them one or two and tell them you cannot remember any more right now. The answer confirms that a candidate has some insight into personal failings.
- Do not use a weakness which could be potentially destructive. To be disorganized and often turn up late for football, is tantamount to be rejected from medical school.
- Do not say you have no weakness as it comes across as being arrogant.

Examples of Weaknesses

- Chose a weakness that can be remedied, i.e. I am very punctual and at times intolerant of people being late.
- Becoming emotionally attached to patients: I currently work as a volunteer in a hospice. I spent a lot of time listening to this particular patient and I had built a rapport with her. She died on my days off. I was deeply saddened by this and I was very upset. I spoke to the ward sister, who told me it was a natural reaction because of my inexperience and that I would get used to it after a while. The sister told me that her relatives had thanked me for the time I had spent by her bedside listening to her concerns. This gave me a strong sense of achievement of having made a difference.

- Burdening myself with too many commitments: I find it very hard to say no to my friends. A few days before my A level Biology exam my friends kept ringing me with questions. Instead of telling them that I was too busy revising I would help them. I am now learning to become more assertive. I am more realistic about my abilities to deliver and more open with my friends.
- In the nursing home, I was over-empathetic to some patients who did not have any relatives.
- Sometimes I used to take criticism too personally. Now, I see criticism as a positive thing and I try to learn from it.
- During my work experience, one of the patients had a stillbirth and had been trying for 10 years for the baby. I was quite upset for her.
- I am sure during my time at medical school I will be trained to cope in these situations.

5   MMI Personal Skills: Personal Qualities

Here are some example questions on Personal Qualities:

- How do you cope with criticism? (Over the years, if my parents or others criticized me, I would take it personally. Now I see criticism in a positive constructive way. I try to learn from it.)
- Give an example in your own life when you showed empathy?
- Give an example where you played an effective role as a team leader?
- How good are your organizational skills?
- How do you manage your time? (Maintaining excellent academic achievement while pursuing a hobby can be evidence of good time management.)
- Give me an example when you were a leader?
- Give me an example when you showed leadership skills?
- How do you cope with stress?
- Can you think of a situation where you were under pressure and how you coped with it?
- Can you demonstrate your ability to cope under pressure and discuss the mechanisms you have adopted to do this?
- If you could change two things about yourself, what would they be?
- Do you have the personality that it takes to do medicine?
- Why should we take you rather than someone else?
- Why are you the best person?

- The study of medicine requires considerable commitment and dedication. What can you tell us about yourself that shows you have this commitment?
- What did you learn from your work experience?

6 MMI Personal Skills: Team Work

Do you work better by yourself or as part of a team?

- I can work well both individually and as part of a team.
- Over the last few years I have been part of several teams.
- I organized a charity event for my local hospice. I took responsibility for collecting the money.
- I play the oboe in my school orchestra. I had to play solo and at other times as part of a group. I needed to interact with my colleagues as part of the orchestra.
- During the summer holidays I work as a sales assistant at Top Shop. I get on well with my colleagues and am always willing to help out when extra help is required.
- Our work is commission based, depending on how many goods we sell. I take responsibility for my share of sales and have always delivered the results asked of me.

7 MMI Personal Skills: Leadership

Give me an example when you show good leadership?

- I do enjoy leading and the sense of accomplishment that comes with it e.g. I led the lacrosse team to victory in the Berkshire county championship.
- I organised all the training and practice well in advance.
- I managed to pull together the team spirit by getting everyone involved in the lacrosse events leading up to the tournament and helping to organise the logistics. This was a difficult time as the exams were coming up. This led me to feel a great sense of achievement.
- One of my strengths is the fact that I have a clear idea of what I want to achieve and am able to bring the other team members on board through my enthusiasm and by involving them in making important decisions. This encourages them to give more of themselves to achieve the team goals.

- I have learnt a great deal about leadership in my school, where I have been given several opportunities to lead in sports and the Duke of Edinburgh expeditions. During our Gold Duke of Edinburgh expeditions, we had ended up in the wrong place and were running very late. Despite being mentally and physically exhausted, I realised that we needed to focus and change tactics if we were to make it to our final destination on time. I pulled everyone together for a meeting and told them we were going to be positive and move on. We went over the map again and we worked out a new route, which everyone was happy with. I led from the front, keeping a fast pace and using my sense of humour to encourage everyone to remain positive. We reached our destinations on time and everyone was very happy.

- I was volunteering at my local hospice and the Matron asked me to do a charity event to make money for the hospice. It was a role I embraced. Having a leadership role amongst my friends and peers meant I was able to recognise and use other team members skills to achieve goals and meet the deadlines we had set. I wrote to the School Governor and asked him for the use of the school dining hall so we could serve food. We had a meeting to discuss who was doing what tasks among the team: e.g.
    - To approach the parents to supply the food.
    - To organise the sponsorship forms and get all the volunteers.
    - To serve the food and clean up afterwards.
    - To organise the local off-licence to supply the wine at wholesale price.
    - To collect the money.

  It was my duty to make sure all the tasks were delegated to the right people and also raise and resolve any trouble shooting issues that were encountered. On the day, I gave a thank you speech. People responded well to my leadership. I believe I led the team in a decisive and assertive fashion whilst maintaining democracy and motivation. We made £3000 for the hospice.

- Last year, I was involved in collecting money for my local hospice. I organized a charity walk and a lunch afterwards. I had a team meeting, which I chaired. I encouraged all the members to come up with ideas of who was going to organize the food, collect the money, organize the use of the school dining hall, clean up afterwards etc. Everyone was very enthusiastic and hardworking. Each had a specific role which they had chosen and they took responsibility for that role. Being approachable, flexible, and a good communicator helped me to make the event a great success.

- Every weekend, I volunteered as a swim coach with groups of young children. This refined my ability to assess individual needs and ensured participants improved. Additionally, my ability to encourage, motivate, and gain the trust of others was important in keeping children relaxed in the water. Last summer, I served as a swim coach. Coaching gave me the opportunities to pass on discipline, determination, and team work skills I gained through my own swimming career.
- I helped found a dance group. Being part of the dance group showed me the importance of open-mindedness, as well as the value of self-expression, collaboration and the commitment that it takes to start a new organization.

8   MMI Personal Skills: Are you a leader or a follower?

- It is very important not to say I am definitely a leader. Some interviewers might think that the NHS is full of leaders and not enough team players.
- It is best to say: I am happy to be a leader and to take the initiative and responsibility when required, but I am equally happy being delegated to, and playing my part as a member of a team.
- As captain of the cricket team, we won the county championship recently. As a good leader, I respected the skills of others, communicated with clarity and supported and encouraged the members. Over the past few years, I have personally been involved in working in different types of teams.
- As a team player in my local football team, I am a hard working, enthusiastic person with a good sense of humour.
- I try to maintain harmony among the team. I work well with different people and can be depended on to promote a positive atmosphere, helping the team to gel.
- In medicine, good, effective teamwork is essential to success.
- In medicine, you work in several different teams. It is essential to know how to work as a team player and a leader.

9   MMI Personal Skills: Leadership and Mistakes

Give us an example of when you were a leader and things went wrong.
Tell us about your greatest mistake.
What did you learn from it?
What would you do differently?

- I was captain of the school cricket team. One of the team players was turning up late for practice and not pulling his weight in the team.
- He was contributing negatively to the team and causing a conflict between other team members.
- In one of the competitions, I was trying to steamroll the team to get quick results. I became impatient with him and I totally overreacted. I started to have a go at him in front of all the team players.
- On reflecting on my experience, I realised afterwards my behaviour was totally inappropriate.
- The crucial mistake I had made was to allow the problem to escalate and hope it would go away.
- I should have met up with him on his own much earlier and had a chat with him and find out why he was not pulling his weight. He might have been burdening himself with too many commitments.
- I should have given him constructive criticism earlier so that we could all move forward together.

10 MMI Personal Skills: Time Management

How do you manage your time?

Maintaining excellent grades while pursing all my hobbies can be evidence of good time management.

11 MMI Personal Skills: Multi-Tasking

Working as a doctor requires you to multi-task. How good are you at multi-tasking?

- I have a lot of experience at multitasking. During the past four years, I have studied for my A levels, worked at the weekends in my local hospital, played in the orchestra and organized a charity event within my school. I also allocated time to meet my friends and socialize. To do this I had to be good at multi-tasking. I use my diary to ensure that everything runs smoothly. To achieve all this, I needed to be very organized and I feel I have demonstrated good organization skills.
- I have been form captain on several occasions. This involved planning and running various activities from house assemblies, quiz nights, to making sure that people did not jump the queue in the dining hall. This was a role which demanded good communication skills, hard work, self-discipline, all of which will be important in my medical career.

- I have successfully kept a balance between my academic and non-academic interests by having varied sporting interests.
- There may be opportunities for you to run societies or clubs at your school. Becoming a prefect or getting involved in mentoring schemes also give you the chance to improve your leadership skills.
- Medical schools are looking for well-rounded, sociable people who will contribute positively to medical school life.

12 MMI Personal Skills: Team Player Example

Give an example when you played the role of a team player?

- Before Christmas I was asked to sell tickets for a charity concert at Southwark Cathedral.
- I realised very early on that I was going to have a problem. Most of the parents could not come because it was so close to Christmas and they had other plans.
- I felt it was crucial to involve the team to see what ideas they could come up with.
- I immediately called the leader and asked for a team meeting. From my experience in working in different teams, I realised the importance of communication in ensuring that obstacles are anticipated and resolved early.
- I told the team the nature of the problem and the progress I had made and said any contributions from the team would be greatly appreciated.
- As a group, we came up with the idea of selling the tickets in our local village square during and after a Christmas Carol Service.
- We managed to sell all the tickets and raised £2000 for charity.
- By being honest with the team and asking for help earlier on, I ensured that we had a very successful concert and raised a lot of money.
- From my work experience, I saw that good, effective teamwork is essential to success.

13 MMI Personal Skills: Resilience: What is resilience?

Resilience is the ability to bounce back from tough times, or even triumph in the face of adversity; to develop tenacity, tolerate ambiguity and stress, have good coping mechanisms, be able to overcome obstacles, be adaptable, flexible with change, and able to compromise.

When have you shown resilience?

As well as all my academic duties, I am fully involved in sports activities, music lessons, orchestra, volunteering, teaching sailing and so on. I am juggling all of these, so I have to be resilient.

How important is resilience in medicine? Doctors need to be resilient to be able to deal with the challenges of medicine.

14 **MMI Personal Skills: What can go wrong in a team?**

Several things can go wrong in a team:

- People not pulling their weight.
- One or two members can dominate the group.
- Some members do not contribute.
- There is lack of clarity regarding goals and specific tasks are not agreed.
- There is lack of trust among the members.
- Some members belittle the ideas of others.
- Roles are not delegated properly.
- People talk more than they listen.
- There are arguments between members of the team, as opposed to constructive difference of opinion.
- Members not willing to take responsibility.
- The leader not identifying the needs of the team members.
- The leader ignoring one of the team players.
- The team having no set goals or deadlines.
- Lack of respect for colleagues e.g. patronising them, ignoring them, or disrespecting them.

15 **MMI Personal Skill Station: Describe a challenge you have overcome.**

- Describe a situation in which you were really stressed and relay how you dealt with it.
- Everyone has overcome a challenge. It is not acceptable to state your life has been perfect.
- You may provide an answer from any area of your life - personal, professional, extracurricular etc. You do not have to be the hero. The key is showing how you came to a decision during a challenging situation and what you learned from it.

16 MMI Personal Skills: Conflict Management

How do you deal with conflict and give an example of when you had conflict and what did you do about it?

- I play the violin in a group and in the orchestra. I try and resolve any issues with my colleagues calmly and rationally so as to avoid conflict. We had three big concerts coming up and we all wanted to play the main solo piece. We had been practising the pieces for quite some time and we all felt ready to play solo. I suggested that as there were three violinists that one of us could play solo at each concert. This helped to maintain harmony among the team members. This helped to promote a positive atmosphere, helping the team to gel.
- During the summer, I worked in Top Shop and one of the customers became very angry with one of my colleagues. I listened carefully to what the customer had to say. I remained calm as she vented and described her side of the story. I apologized for the inconvenience. I asked if she wanted to speak to the manager. She was content that I had heard her out and said everything was fine.

17 MMI Personal Skills: Accomplishments

What have you accomplished?
What is your greatest/proudest/most memorable achievement?
Give us an example of when you showed commitment.
Give us an example when you showed dedication.

You must use these questions as an opportunity to demonstrate what you have gained and how you have learnt from the experience. Think of a hobby or interest where you utilise one of the following skills, and consider how useful it will be for medicine:
- Team player
- Leadership
- Coping with pressure
- Organisational skills
- Multi-tasking

It is important to let them know the amount of dedication and the hours that are needed to gain such an achievement e.g.

- I see my accomplishments as being in three areas: I have received top grades in my GCSE, ASs and A levels. I have achieved a Diploma in piano and I sing in a band leading to a charity recital in my local town hall to raise money for cancer research. My greatest achievement is my academic and music results, and being able to get all my medical work experience, as a result of a lot of time and hard work. To do this I had to be organized, be able to deal with conflicting demands on my time, hard work, enthusiasm, motivation, and ability to work as part of a team. Also, I organized a charity walk for my local hospice. The fun was forming the team and helping to delegate roles. The hardest part was constantly nagging people for the money. Through a lot of effort, we produced a successful event and we raised over £1,500.

- I have received top grades in my examinations. In the community I have spent three years working in a hospice. In music I have achieved Grade 8 in the oboe leading to a charity recital where we received £2,000. I took responsibility for organizing the charity.

- We had inter-school competitions that required communication and organization with outside companies. I had to coordinate the tasks and delegate the work.

- Having passed stage 4 RYA Youth Sailing course, I signed up as a member of Upton Warren Sailing Club and took part in the club regatta. I have learnt a lot about myself in terms of determination, preparation and endurance in all conditions. I have trained continuously for the last six years and qualified at each stage. It was a gruelling regime, three times a week after a long day at school and every Saturday. The weather conditions were often very difficult. Every Saturday, I sail with the sailing club and compete against other sailing clubs around the UK. I have to be at the club at 8 a.m. I developed qualities of self-discipline and commitment from persevering until I reached my final sailing exam. I am now an instructor providing students with a range of skills and knowledge to help them become confident sailors. As a leader, I make it fun and sociable. I maintain their interest, enthusiasm, and ultimately their participation. I show enthusiasm, drive, talent and commitment to the sport. Being organised and good at time management was absolutely crucial to my sailing development. I had to very organised and good at multi-tasking as I had to work around my other sports and work experience. It also improved my confidence. These will be very good transferable skills which I can use in medicine.

- I have achieved a Grade 8 with a distinction in the piano, leading to a charity recital in my local shopping centre to raise money for cancer research UK.

- Over the last four years, my martial arts training developed my physical and mental stamina and culminated in a black belt in kickboxing. It was a tough regime and it was physically very demanding. I had to apply myself regularly and consistently four times a week after a long day at school. In medicine, this will help me deal with the physical and emotional challenges.

18 MMI Personal Skills: Commitment

In what way are you committed?

- Over the last five years, I have played the oboe in the orchestra and I play guitar and sing in my band. I enjoy playing the guitar and have recently passed my grade 8. This has involved a disciplined approach to practice daily.
- I also had to be well organized to fit in all my lessons and practice schedules, while still doing my A levels and my weekend job. In the orchestra, we played in concert for three hours on a Sunday at Southwark Cathedral, and on Monday morning I had my A level Biology exam.

19 MMI Personal Skills: Why not Nursing

Why not nursing, or pharmacy, or physiotherapy?

Never criticise nurses. Nurses do a great job.

- I want to do medicine because I like the in depth knowledge challenge of being able to diagnose and prescribe treatment. Medicine offers a more academic course.
- I like the role of diagnosing, carrying out investigations and formulating a treatment plan.

20 MMI Personal Skills: Multi-Disciplinary Team

Who are the most important members of the multi-disciplinary team?

- All the team members and the team leader are the most important members of a team.
- In the nursing home where I worked, the patient had fallen and fractured her femur. Both the occupational therapist and the social

workers were very important. The occupational therapist assessed the patient's ability to cope with day-to-day tasks, and made recommendations to make them easier, bearing in mind her reduced mobility. Social workers arranged additional help by having carers to do the washing and dressing, which she was struggling to perform by herself in the ward.

- The palliative care team and Macmillan nurses play a crucial role for patients with terminal cancer.

21 MMI Personal Skills: Team Players

As a doctor, whom would you regard as part of the team?

Doctors, nurses, healthcare assistants, patients, physiotherapists, dieticians, radiologists, different types of managers, receptionists and secretaries are all part of a team.

During my work experience one of the patients had bowel cancer. The doctors arranged a meeting with the multi-disciplinary team to establish the best treatment for the patient. The team was made up of surgeons, anaesthetist, dieticians, physiotherapists, nurses, psychiatrists and oncologists. They ensured that his care was well coordinated, and that all his needs were attended to.

22 MMI Personal Skills: Compassion

What is compassion? Compassion, which begins with empathy, is an essential element in the doctor-patient relationship. It involves being curious about the patient's symptoms and views, being present, attentive, and respectful to the patient, caring and offering your support.

How do you know you are compassionate?

- I think my compassion is best reflected in the day–to-day way I live: I help to explain science concepts to class mates who are finding things more difficult. Every Thursday after school, I teach a group of children who have learning difficulties.

23 MMI Personal Skills: Personal Description

If you were a doctor, how would you like your patients to describe you?

- Of all the descriptions I would probably say professional, caring, dedicated, focused, approachable, organized, good listening skills, competent, good communication skills.

24 MMI Personal Skills: Organization Skills

How good are your organizational skills?

- Over the past two years, whilst studying for my A Levels, I did volunteering work experience in the hospice, played in the orchestra every Saturday, performed in a group and on Sunday I taught sailing. To achieve all this, I needed to be very organized and have good organizational skills.
- On one occasion, I had to play in the orchestra for four hours on a Sunday and sit my A level Biology exam the following morning.
- Being meticulous and organized has really helped me minimize stress by enabling me to achieve everything I needed to achieve: as a result I feel equipped to deal with the pressure of studying medicine.

25 MMI Personal Skills: Team Work

What are the advantages and disadvantages of working in a team?

Advantages:

- Improves efficiency and quality of care delivered, due to a combined knowledge and skill mix.
- Able to spread the workload through delegation to others.
- Improves quality of decision making.
- Encourages creativity.
- Provides a supportive environment and encourages learning and personal development.
- Improves team moral and job satisfaction.
- Reduces stress.
- Able to rely on the support of others if you require assistance.

<u>Disadvantages</u>:

- Some team members rely on the energy and enthusiasm of the committed.
- If the leader is absent, work can stop.
- Some members may resent the way they are treated in the group, leading to high absenteeism and staff turnover.
- Will only function if there is a strong leader - some team members may be left feeling confused and leaderless.
- Some team players may not like rewards being shared with others.

26 MMI Personal Skills: What makes a good Team

What makes a good team?

- A good team needs both good team members and a good team leader.
- One of the key challenges to any good team is to make sure that everyone pulls their weight.
- You need a team who are hardworking, enthusiastic, reliable and motivated to get the work done.
- They like to move things along by suggesting ideas, clarifying the ideas of others and confronting problems.
- They need to be flexible and adaptable to any changing deadlines and plans.
- All team members are clear about the team objectives and their own role in meeting those objectives.
- They need to be good listeners, considerate and able to compromise.
- They need to be punctual and reliable with deadlines.
- They communicate effectively within and outside the team.
- The team's performance is regularly reviewed and any areas of improvement are identified and addressed.
- On top of that, a good team will require a leader who leads by example and is enthusiastic, hardworking competent, with a good sense of humour and encourages his team to reach their goals.
- He must have clear objectives and aspirations and anticipate potential areas of conflict.
- A good team leader is a decision-maker and can see the reasons for change and will implement these changes.
- Has initiative and resilience to cope with setbacks and adapts to rapidly changing circumstances.

- Knows the strengths and weaknesses of each team member, so he can pool the strength of team members effectively.
- Motivates and encourages each member of the team to give 100%.

27 MMI Personal Skills: Personal Qualities

What are your qualities?

- From my work experience, I realized I have a lot of transferable skills which will help me in medicine.

List the first six qualities, and when you are talking about your leadership skills; you must introduce situations where you have demonstrated these skills e.g. I am hard working, motivated, caring, compassionate with good communication skills. I am a good team player, good team leader, I am organized and good at multi-tasking:

- As a member of the football team, I …
- As captain of the cricket team, I …
- Over the last three to four years, I studied for my exams, did my voluntary work, played oboe in the orchestra, was a lead singer in the band, and worked every Saturday in Top Shop. To do this, I had to be very organized and good at multi-tasking.

It is very important to put the six Cs in your qualities: Care, Compassion, Communication, Competence, Committment, Courage.

The key to juggling all your activities is good organization, multi-tasking, time management and planning. Show them you have time designated to: yourself, your sports, music, friends and you are a well-rounded individual.

28 MMI Personal Skills: Reaction to Failure

How do you react to failure?

Give an example (e.g. Academic prizes, Awards, Driving test). Try to make it something which was important to win. Overcoming emotional failure is difficult and makes you a stronger person. You can fail, work hard to overcome it and subsequently succeed. Refer to these in your answer:
- It was painful

- I really wanted it
- I was upset for a while
- I changed my approach
- The whole experience was hard, but I learned from it.

What would you do if you had several tasks to do and not enough time to do them?

- It is important to recognize with this type of question that you cannot be in more than one place at the same time.
- It is assessing your ability to communicate and work as a team.
- I would rapidly assess and prioritise patients, and identify sick patients who require my immediate help.
- I would coordinate the efforts of other members of the team.
- I would recognise my limits and ask for help from other specialists or my consultant.
- With effective communication, prioritising, delegating, and asking for help early, the scenario would be managed successfully with no detrimental impact on patient care.

29 MMI Personal Skills: Positive and Negatives

What attracts you the most and the least about our medical school?

Mention all the positives.

For negatives, say that you expect to come across a few during your five years of study.

Always end on a positive note, i.e. "after the open day and speaking to the medical students, I am really looking forward to coming here".

30 MMI Personal Skills: Challenges

What challenges do you think a career in medicine will bring you?

- I think it will be intellectually, emotionally, and physically challenging.
- During my work experience shadowing a gynaecologist/obstetrician, there was a great feeling of satisfaction helping to deliver a healthy baby and the family were very excited. An hour later, another patient had a stillbirth and I was devastated.

- The doctor's bleep was going constantly, and she had to make difficult decisions at very short notice.
- The doctor needs to be able to work with different teams either as a team player or a team leader. The team needs to be well-coordinated and work well together to benefit the patient.
- To be able to communicate with people at all levels. Deal with patients who are violent, patients with unreasonable expectations, and with vulnerable and distressed patients.
- Work long and unsocial hours.
- Be able to tell patients bad news.
- Deal with the stress of having to prepare and study for exams, whilst maintaining clinical duties.
- Deal with the unexpected.
- Manage complaints from patients and relatives, which may involve lots of paperwork.
- Manage with limited resources.
- Be able to tell a patient he cannot have a particular cancer drug because he lives in the wrong area.
- Be able to audit your practice.
- Spend time training junior doctors and medical students. It is important to have good communication skills.
- You must continually update your skills and knowledge.
- You may be involved in research.
- Doctors are constantly under public scrutiny.

31 MMI Personal Skills: Pros and Cons of being a Doctor

What are the pros and cons of being a doctor?

Pros
- I think I will enjoy the buzz of working as part of a team.
- Working with colleagues and other health professionals, pulling our expertise together for the good of the patient.
- Doing research.
- Treating patients and making a difference to their lives.
- Continuous learning.
- Enjoying the variety in the work and the intellectual challenges.
- There are many opportunities to use leadership and organizational skills.
- Teaching opportunities.

Cons
- Need to manage with limited resources
- Often one has to deal with uncertainty
- Patients may have unreasonable expectations
- Sometimes, doctors can become too involved emotionally with patient care
- Exposed to long hours
- Changing shift patterns
- Having a realistic appreciation of the physical, academic and emotional demand of medicine has made me carefully consider my motivations to be a doctor and has only affirmed my resolve to study medicine.

32 MMI Personal Skills Station: Discouraging someone from Medicine

How would you dissuade someone from going into medicine?
- Tell them about the long five years of training.
- Medicine involves lots of hard work, stress, deadlines, and exams.
- There is a lot of pressure, and hours can often be irregular.
- You need to be a hard worker with lots of stamina.
- You need to be organized, be able to multitask, be able to cope well under pressure and to deal with stress.
- Medicine offers a way to develop your love of science, but if you have the above qualities, you can look forward to the challenges.

33 MMI Personal Skills: Becoming a Doctor

What are you looking forward to most and least about becoming a doctor?

- I am looking forward to further enhancing my clinical skills, communication, and knowledge.
- To be able to use a problem solving approach to diagnose a patient.
- I will enjoy observing the patient satisfaction after successful surgery.
- I look forward to the feeling of satisfaction when you deliver a healthy baby.
- Being able to work as part of different teams.
- I like the idea of continuous learning.
- Building a good rapport with the patients.
- Dealing with the emotional and physical challenges of medicine.
- There are difficulties being a doctor e.g. "I am a caring and empathetic person and I would find it hard to tell a patient that she cannot have a

cancer drug because she lived in a particular area or to tell a patient that they had six months to live".

34 MMI Personal Skills: Communication Skills

How would you rate your communication skills?

- Over the past few years, I have developed good communication skills. I worked in a nursing home where one of the patients had Alzheimer's. Her daughter and grandchildren found it very frustrating and upsetting when she did not recognize them. I felt I made a real difference by simply listening to the daughter and allowing her to cry and get it all out.
- In my Duke of Edinburgh expedition, I developed good skills in being upfront about problems and making sure that everyone in the team knew what everyone else was doing and what equipment we were carrying.

35 MMI Personal Skills: Empathy

What is empathy?

- Empathy is the ability to put yourself in other people's shoes.
- Empathy is about being sensitive and attentive, and acknowledging patient's needs, in a warm and caring manner.
- Empathy is also about creating a safe environment for patients, and checking that their needs are satisfied.

Are you an empathetic person?
Give me an example of when you showed empathy?

- During my work experience in my local hospital, a young mother of three young children was just diagnosed with cervical cancer and given six months to live. She was devastated. I spent a lot of time listening to all her concerns about leaving her children and husband behind, and her fear of dying. I put myself in her shoes and really felt how difficult her situation was. I began to understand her anxieties and fears. She told the doctor that it helped her enormously being able to get it all off her chest and how understanding I was.
- My friend's grandmother died suddenly and my friend did not have time

to say goodbye. She was devastated. I sat with my friend for hours and listened to her. I knew what it was like because my grandfather had died suddenly a few years ago.

Are you born with empathy?

- I think you are born with some empathy but you also develop it over the course of your life.

How important is empathy in medicine?

- From my work experience, I saw the importance of empathy. (Always 4-5 points on these answers.)
- It facilitates a more accurate diagnosis as the patient will be more honest about their lifestyle; for example, about how much they drink and smoke, and it creates a more caring environment.
- It plays a vital role in the patient's experience, and is a key component of the doctor-patient relationship,
- I saw on the wards how empathy is the crux of a good therapeutic relationship; it helped to establish rapport, and it enhanced the patient's experience. Before and during procedures; the doctor explained everything to the patient, communicating clearly and sensitively, using an empathetic approach, constantly reassuring them, and making the patient feel at ease.
- In the GP practice, the way the doctors expressed empathy is highly effective and powerful; it builds patient trust, calms anxiety, and improves health outcomes.
- The GP explained that empathy is associated with better adherence to medications, and increased patient satisfaction.
- The GP told me that a patient's feelings, concerns, expectations and ideas are just as important as a presenting physical complaint. By engaging with the patient, a doctor can better understand these things, and ultimately provide better care.
- From speaking to patients, I was impressed how even the smallest expressions of empathy made such a huge, lasting impression. Patients may be at their most vulnerable, and at their lowest possible moment in life. They find it easier to open up and discuss their concerns with somebody who is caring empathetically for them, and has taken the time to try to understand what they are going through.
- Empathy is therefore important because it helps to make the patient

feel more at ease, enables a doctor to understand how the patient may be feeling, and what the patient may be expecting in terms of clinical outcome.

What is the difference between empathy and sympathy?

- Empathy is when you imagine you are the patient and put yourself in their situation. You think how the patient will be feeling in their current situation. Sympathy is when you feel sorry for the patient and pity him.

36 MMI Personal Skills: Stress

How do you deal with stress?

When asked this question, draw from your past experience. Do not say you have never experienced stress. Stress management is crucial to be able to succeed in the medical profession. Medicine can be incredibly stressful at times, and the profession tends to place you in positions that will push you to your limit.

- I have learnt to deal with stress in many different ways. If I think I am getting stressed, I reassess the situation. I use my diary to make sure I have time for myself.
- The key for me (juggling all my academic, extra-curriculum, sports and my weekend job and still finding time for myself) lies in good organization and planning.
- From time to time, I consider my current work priorities and expectations and I ask myself if they are realistic.
- Studying for my GCSEs and A-levels and Grade 8 music exams is stressful. Going to the gym three times a week helped me to release my frustrations and relieve stress.
- I am involved in many extra-curricular activities: I play the oboe in my school orchestra; I am captain of my school hockey team. To manage (my academics, my sailing and all my sports I have to be very organized and good at multi-tasking) I keep a diary and I factor in regular breaks and relaxation time.
- You should give an example and reflect on the situation, discussing the strategies you used to successfully manage the situation, as well as how you may deal with the similar situation differently in the future.

37 MMI Personal Skills: Why You?

Why should we take you rather than someone else?

- I consider myself to be a well-rounded dynamic student with a realistic view of what medicine is about and with significant relevant experience and I look forward to the challenges and rewards of medicine.
- From my work experience, I feel I can appreciate the varied nature of medical practice. In the process, I develop a great understanding of the pace and pressure of working as part of a team, the intellectual, the emotional, and the physical challenges of medicine, the long hours, and dealing with conflicting demands.
- I have an ability to balance commitments.
- By talking to staff and medical students about studying and practicing medicine, I have gained a valuable insight to the workings of a busy hospital and the hectic life of a doctor. There are also many elements of the job which doctors enjoy.
- My self-discipline has been tested by having to divide my time between work, school, playing in the hockey team, being form captain, the school orchestra and concert band.
- I've built up the ability to work well in a team with a common aim.
- An appreciation of the communication skills and an understanding of teamwork required in medicine.
- Leading a team has helped me learn how to communicate my ideas, and has honed my leadership skills because of the need to motivate and inspire others.
- I have a thorough awareness of the realities of medicine
- I am a caring and compassionate person.
- I like to challenge and push myself.

38 MMI Personal Skills: Decision Making

Describe a time when you made a life changing decision?
- I was deciding between Law and Medicine. Over the last two years of different work experience, I knew medicine was definitely for me.

39 MMI Personal Skills: Applicant Questions

Which question would you most want to ask, if you were interviewing an applicant for a place at medical school?

- I would ask the applicant what is the extent of his motivation for medicine and if he thinks he has a realistic view of what medicine is all about.
- Tell me about yourself.
- What have you gained from your work experience?
- How do you cope with stress?
- How do you work as part of a team?
- Tell me about your organizational skills.

40 MMI Personal Skills: To be a Medical Student

Do you know what is it like to be a medical student?

- I have a good idea of what is in store for me. From attending open days, reading the prospectus, talking to students and doctors, I feel I have a good idea of what is awaiting me.
- During my work experience on the wards, the medical students were very open about how hard and stressful the course can be at times. They talked about the workshops, lectures, seminars and clinical visits they had to attend. It was clear that students have to work both alone and with others. The students discussed the OSCE with me. They emphasized how important it is to practice skills from day one.
- My self-discipline has been tested by having to divide my time between work, school, playing hockey, being form captain and prefect, school orchestra and wind band.
- Leading a team has helped me improve my communication skills, it has honed my leadership skills because of the continual need to motivate and inspire others.
- Being someone who is very good at multi-tasking, I feel I am ready to be a medical student.

41 MMI Personal Skills: Being a Medical Student

What makes you think that you can cope with being a medical student?

- Over the last few years, I studied for my A levels, passed Grade 8 oboe music exams, was captain of the school hockey team, was form captain and prefect, and worked weekends at my local hospice. To do this, I had to be very organized, and self-disciplined with good time management skills.

- I have several mechanisms to deal with stress and pressure. I go to the gym, play tennis, and am captain of the hockey team. I read and listen to music.
- Having spoken to medical students, I feel I have a very realistic view of what medical school is all about and the stress involved. I feel I am up for the challenge.

42 MMI Personal Skills: Qualities of a Good Doctor

What are the qualities of a good doctor?

When you are asked the qualities of doctor, it is very important that you always relate back to your work experience. So, state that, from your work experience, you saw the qualities of a good doctor:

- Needs to be knowledgeable and up to date with their knowledge.
- Hard working, motivated with lots of stamina.
- Caring, compassionate, committed with good communication skills (4 Cs)
- Can cope under immense pressures, organised and methodical.
- Have a logical and enquiring mind,
- Works as a team player,
- Have a flair for leadership and management.
- Is good at multi-tasking.
- A thoughtful and caring approach to communication with patients, their relatives and work colleagues,
- A lifelong approach to learning.
- Needs to be inquisitive, and wants to keep up to date with the latest trends and treatments in medicine.
- Resilient and adaptable.
- Be able to deal with the emotional and physical challenges of medicine.
- Be an excellent communicator—can deal with people at all levels, have good listening skills, and be able to build a good rapport with patients and colleagues.
- Be able to cope under pressure and maintain a good work-life balance.
- Capacity to manage time and prioritise workload.
- Able to recognise his limitations and know when to seek help from his senior colleagues.
- Has a sense of humour.

43 MMI Personal Skills: Personal Insight into Medicine

What are the physical, emotional and intellectual challenges of medicine?
What pressures do you think doctors face in their professional and personal lives?
What might be the negative side to working as a doctor?
What are the downsides of a career in medicine?
Why do doctors need to be resilient?

It is very important that you are aware of the realities of medicine. During your work experience, it is important that you appreciate the varied nature of medical practice. You must develop a greater understanding of the pace and pressure of working as part of a team, the intellectual, emotional, ethical and physical challenges of medicine. Write down all the challenges you saw during your work experience e.g.

Physical Challenges:
- Long and unsociable hours,
- On call shifts that would include evenings, weekends and nights.
- The physical element, which involves seeing blood, injuries, suffering and death.
- The doctor's bleeper going constantly, running from ward to ward, and having to make difficult decisions at short notice.
- Everyone was looking for the doctor—the nurses, his team, relatives and the patients.
- Having to deal with several tasks, urgent requests and tight deadlines.
- He had lots of paperwork, writing up charts, discharging patients, taking bloods etc.
- Dealing with angry, violent, upset or demanding patients.
- Long hours standing in theatre.

Emotional Challenges:
- Having to tell someone bad news.
- On the Oncology ward, the doctor's feeling of powerlessness for some patients with poor outcome.
- On the paediatric ward, having to tell parents that their child has leukaemia.
- If you worked on the Obstetrics/Gynaecology ward:
- The doctor dealing with the excitement of helping a woman safely deliver her baby, and then having to console a patient who has a still birth.

- The doctor help patients through particularly difficult times when dealing with miscarriages, undergoing hysterectomies and battling terminal cancer.
- Having to tell a patient that she had miscarried for the fourth time.
- Not being able to cure a patient.

Intellectual Challenges:
- Many years of study
- A doctor needs a good and long lasting memory
- Lifelong learning and keeping up to date.
- Often dealing with uncertainty.
- Work life balance can sometimes suffer.

Ethical challenges:
- Issues around abortion, child protection, confidentiality etc.

44 MMI Personal Skills: Potential Problems

What do you think you will struggle most with at our medical school? What potential problems do you anticipate?

I understand that university involves a lot of hard work and, initially, it may be difficult to balance academic study with getting involved in lots of clubs and societies, but using my organizational and time-management skills and being a motivated and conscientious person, I feel equipped to take on these challenges.

CHAPTER 10

MMI WORK EXPERIENCE

As mentioned several times in this book, work experience is essential to get into medical school. It is vital to test your interest in medicine by spending time with vulnerable patients, and observe what the doctors do on a daily basis. The perspectives you gain from working in the real world with real people are invaluable in providing understanding and compassionate care. The medical schools are searching for well rounded, caring applicants. For medical schools admissions, the type of work experience placements form a crucial part of assessing an applicant's suitability for medicine. You must maximize the benefits from your work experience.

Look for ways to extend yourself. Challenge yourself with a different array of experiences and thus distinguish yourself as someone with the independent mind and the inquisitive spirit most sought after by medical school admissions. Several students, who have always wanted to do medicine, change their mind after a few days of work experience.

You can reflect on your work experiences and define how it led you to your discovery of a passion for medicine.

Keep a detailed diary of your work experience. It will become an invaluable document when you begin preparing for interview questions and your personal statement. It will help you recall what you learnt and allow you to reflect on how it affected you, your motivation for medicine, and your understanding of life as a doctor.

It is likely to be eighteen months to two years before you are interviewed. Start your work experience immediately after your GCSE. Try to get work experience that involves the gritty, unglamorous side of patient care (e.g. giving bedpans, working as a health care assistant, etc.)

Obtain a breadth of work experiences, encompassing medicine both in the hospital, GP, nursing home and hospice. Long term volunteering in a hospice and nursing home shows great commitment to medicine. You can also work in youth centres, HIV unit, summer camps, in a morgue, charitable organisations, church volunteering, with the homeless, caring for children with learning difficulties, working with children or adults with disabilities, St John Ambulance and the Red Cross, charity and fundraising work, with the elderly in the community, League of Friends and many more.

You must take the initiative and ask lots of questions. Why not ask patients what they think makes a good doctor? If you witness any procedures, talk to the patient about how it was for them.

Examples of 19 Work Experience questions and sample answers follow, and for ease of reference, they are listed in Annex 4 to this book.

1   **MMI Work Experience: What did you learn from your work experience?**

This is the most common question asked every year at medical school interviews. Recognise the skills that you have that reflect those of a good doctor. Make the most of your work experience. If you see a procedure ask the F1 about it. You must pursue information about what you see. Write down the signs and symptoms and what tests are available to confirm the diagnosis. Get to know the patients and talk to them about their experience of hospital life, their condition and its impact on their lives, etc.

- During my work experience, I developed a greater understanding of the pace and pressure of working as part of a team, the emotional and physical challenges of medicine, the long hours and dealing with conflicting demands.
- In surgery, I saw the importance of combining medical knowledge, precision in procedures, good communication and interaction skills.
- I got to talk to doctors and medical students about the good and bad side of their course.
- I saw doctors diagnose a patient from a set of often unclear, ambiguous or contradictory facts or symptoms.
- Observing ward rounds made me realize that good communication with the patient is essential.
- Much of the anxiety stems from the uncertainty and lack of information about their condition.

- I enjoyed the variety of work, the continuous learning, and the buzz of working in a team.

2   MMI Work Experience: Nursing Home

What did you learn from the Nursing Home?

In the past two years, I have developed crucial communications skills whilst volunteering in a nursing home. I learnt:
- To be more considerate and to be aware of the difficulties people encounter as they become older.
- It highlighted the complex clinical and social needs of our increasingly elderly population.
- I found chatting with them developed my patience and ability to empathise, encouraging me to consider individual needs.
- By listening to patients, I witnessed the different ways in which an illness can impact on someone.
- I witnessed first-hand the impact illness can have on a patient's dignity and the effect it has on both themselves and their relatives.
- One of the patients had Alzheimer's and her daughter would get very upset, when one day her mother would recognise her, and a few hours later she had no idea who she was. She would cry and let all her frustrations out.
- I observed the distressing effects of chronic illness and the increasing health care needs of the ageing population, with the harsh reality that medicine cannot cure all.
- I felt I made a real difference to their quality of life, simply lending an empathetic ear to their problems and reacting in a caring and patient manner.
- Speaking to relatives and staff improved my interpersonal skills, so that I can comfortably communicate with people of diverse ages, cultures and background.

3   MMI Work Experience: Nursing Home

What did you do in the Nursing Home?

- In the nursing home, I worked alongside the nurses and helped with washing, dressing and caring for the personal needs of the patients.

- A lot of the patients were incapable of looking after themselves. I had to feed them and help them to the toilet.
- Often just talking to the patients whilst brushing their hair, or attending to their needs, made me feel I had made a difference to their day
- Taking patients' vital signs and maintaining food and fluid charts.
- Duties included assisting patients with mobility.

4 MMI Work Experience: Hospice

What did you learn from your work experience in the Hospice?

- In caring for those awaiting death, I have, above all, learnt the true meaning of empathy and concern for the suffering.
- Witnessing the breaking of bad news revealed the importance of being a good listener and being able to communicate clearly and sensitively.
- I observed various patients at different stages of their disease, some during chemotherapy.
- This has exposed me to some of the emotionally challenging aspects of medicine, providing me with many opportunities to speak to patients and relatives and try to cater for different needs, so people can enjoy a more comfortable and dignified life.
- One of the patients was thirty five years old and had been given six months to live. I spent a lot of time at her bedside listening to her concerns. I sensed through what she was saying that she was scared of dying, scared of leaving her two young children behind and she was feeling very isolated and lonely. I put myself in her shoes and really felt how difficult this must be for her. Through this, I began to understand her loneliness, her anxiety and fears.
- As I listened to patients in palliative care, I am cognizant of the crucial role compassionate medicine plays at the end of life.
- Some of the patients told me that I had brightened up their day and helped them through simply by being there and showing some care and attention.
- I learnt the importance of teamwork and communication skills in effective doctor/patient relationship.
- The calm and collective manner in which the doctors dealt with the patient to alleviate suffering truly inspired and enlightened me.

5   **MMI Work Experience: Work Experience Abroad**

What did you learn from your work experience in India?

- In India, working in a hospital was humbling and disheartening.
- I learnt the importance of compassion and empathy, in order to develop a good doctor patient relationship whether I was in India or the UK.
- I gained a profound insight into the great contrast between cultures.
- In both countries, I witnessed the incredible dedication to restore the health of the patient.
- I was struck by the impact of poverty, malnutrition and lack of hygiene, and the high incidence of diseases such as cholera.
- Dealing with patients from various cultural background has highlighted the importance of good communication, in transcending such boundaries, to deliver effective patient care.
- I was touched by the doctor's sensitivity to complex social issues, such as the patient's socio-economic status when deciding on the treatment.
- I saw the difficulty of working in intense conditions with limited resources.
- This was not helped by the poor infrastructure and shortages of doctors and nurses.

6   **MMI Work Experience: Challenges of India**

What challenged you most about your work experience in India?

- It was emotionally challenging.
- Lack of basic resources in the hospital meant that it was often difficult for the doctors to efficiently treat patients.
- I shadowed a surgeon where the contrasting lack of facilities with a UK hospital was clear.
- I felt bad about the limitations enforced upon the patients by their circumstances.
- Some of the patients who died would have survived if they had been treated in the UK.
- Some of the patients had travelled for five to six hours in the excessive heat to get to the hospital and had to wait for hours to be seen, with no air conditioning.
- I have developed a unique perspective about the pervasive inequality in medicine.

- I witnessed how lack of information about preventable infectious diseases often needlessly claimed lives.
- From my work experience in India, I have gained a unique global perspective and a greater cultural awareness that I can apply to my work with diverse patient population.
- My diverse clinical experience in UK and India have solidified my desire to become a doctor.

7 MMI Work Experience: GP Experience

Questions you may be asked about your work experience with a GP.

- What is the role of a GP?
- What is holistic medicine?
- Give examples when you saw holistic medicine in the GP practice.
- What are the frustrations of a GP?
- Should GPs be in charge of the NHS budget?
- What are your views of the NHS changes?
- What did you like most and least about working in the GP practice?
- Did you see the GP tell bad news to the patient?
- How would you tell bad news to a patient?
- Apart from treating patients what else does a GP do? A GP is also involved in education, preventive, managing and monitoring chronic diseases, minor surgery, home visits practice, management and administration, etc.
- What qualities should a GP have?
- How important is communication for a GP?
- What is the difference between a hospital doctor and a GP?
- Is it more important for a surgeon or a GP to have good communications skills?
- Should immunisation be made compulsory?
- If you were a GP how would you deal with an angry patient?
- An HIV positive patient was bleeding from a laceration and needed urgent treatment. You do not have gloves. Would you put the patient or your own safety first?
- In the GP practice who is part of the team?
- How important is team working in the practice?
- Who is the most important person in the team?
- We have an obesity epidemic in the UK. How can GPs help in reducing this epidemic?

- Should GPs be allowed to end the lives of terminal ill patients?
- What is empathy?
- Is it right for doctors to show empathy to their patients?
- What is the difference between empathy and sympathy?
- Give me an example of when the GP showed empathy to the patient.
- Give me an example of when you showed empathy to a patient.
- Give me an example of when you show empathy in your personal life.
- Some NHS Trusts will not put obese patients and patients who smoke on the waiting lists until they lose weight or give up smoking. What are your views on this?
- What are the problems with the elderly population living longer?
- Some nurses in GP practices are doing the role of doctors? What are your views on this? How does this affect the patients?
- GPs are dealing with varied patients of all ages, and from varied cultural and social backgrounds. What qualities do they need?
- When would a GP break confidentiality?
- A patient visits his GP and tells him he is HIV Positive and doesn't want his wife to know. What would you do?
- A 14-year-old girl wants an abortion and does not want you to tell her parents. What would you do?
- What is Gillick/ Fraser competence?
- Is it ever acceptable to lie to a patient?
- Why would a GP take a patient's Blood Pressure?
- What are the complications of high blood pressure?
- How would a GP manage a patient on statins?
- Your patient has ordered drugs on the internet and he thinks they are amazing. What would you say to him?
- An elderly man refuses to take his medication following a heart attack. He presents to your practice with his wife who is very angry with him. What are the issues here?
- How long does it take to train as a GP?

8   MMI Work Experience: Role of the Patient

What is the role of the patient in the multi-disciplinary team?

The patient has a big role in the multi-disciplinary team. During the second half of the twentieth century, the doctor/patient relationship has evolved towards shared decision making. This model respects the patient as an autonomous person with a right to hold views, to make choices, and to take actions based on personal values and beliefs. Patients have been increasingly entitled to weigh the benefits and risks of alternative treatment, including the alternative of no treatment; and to select the alternative that best promotes their own values.

9 MMI Work Experience: Disabled Patient

How would you treat a disabled patient?

Disabled patients are frequently presumed to be incompetent. Labelling patients as disabled is not helpful. No two disabled people are the same. They are individuals. Treat them and talk to them in a normal manner. See past the disability and see the individual. If a patient is deaf, use your hands to explain, or draw a diagram.

10 MMI Work Experience: Communication

How important is communication in medicine?

- Communication is extremely important in medicine. Doctors need to communicate clearly and sensitively with patients and their relatives, as well as with all the rest of the members of the multi-disciplinary team.
- Good listening skills are linked to empathy and should result in better rapport with patients, thereby generating mutual trust and a better working relationship.
- Good active listening skills:
- Use appropriate body language such as an open posture and maintaining good eye contact.
- Show warmth and be supportive and caring.
- Know when to stay quiet.
- A doctor should also be able to convey messages to junior and senior colleagues, as well as to patients and relatives in an effective and clear manner.
- Doctors should be able to adapt their communication to their audience.
- When conveying messages, doctors should:
- Use clear and unambiguous language, avoiding the unnecessary use of jargon.
- Use a variety of communication media in addition to the spoken word such as the written word, diagrams and posters.
- Check the understanding of the audience, if necessary adapting their message.

- There are different forms of communication, including spoken, written, and electronic methods.
- You have to communicate with vulnerable people, including those suffering from disabilities such as deafness and blindness, and with individuals who cannot speak English, or who come from a very different cultural background.
- It is important to keep a formal record of telephone conversations.

11 MMI Work Experience: Motivation for Medicine

Why Medicine?

This is the question that students hate the most. This question should not be answered without significant reference from your work experience. Medical schools want to know have you seen the realities of medicine during your work experience.

Just choose three or four reasons from the following:

- I think medicine is a perfect fit for my interests.
- I have always loved science and the day-to-day interaction with people.
- To make sure medicine is for me, I did several different types of work experience.
- From my work experience, I saw the physical and emotional challenges of medicine.
- From my work experience, I developed awareness of the responsibilities, challenges, trials and tribulations of what it means to be a doctor.
- I spoke to several doctors and medical students and they made me aware of the reality of medicine, the very long training process and all the negative aspects of medicine.
- I was inspired by the scientific approach of doctors when talking among themselves and having to use facts to diagnose a patient.
- I noticed how doctors must think critically to synthesize information, and to solve problems.
- They sometimes have to find out a diagnosis from a set of often unclear, ambiguous or contradictory facts or symptoms.
- I loved the variety of work, the continuous learning, to be able to use a solving problem approach to diagnose a patient.
- I enjoy the challenge of lifelong learning and the excitement of keeping up to date with latest cutting edge medical advances.

- I have a very inquisitive mind and I love the idea of continuous learning and working in an intellectually challenging environment.
- The buzz of working in teams with people with many skills and personalities.
- I have acquired a number of transferable skills in my sports, music and work experience which will help me in medicine.
- I saw how the doctors provide the continuity of care and I saw the compassion shown by them in establishing a trusting rapport with patients.
- During my work experience, I spent a lot of time talking to patients and relatives and I feel proud of the beneficial effect I had on them.
- I thought about the implications of being a doctor and realised what I would be letting myself in for.
- From my work experience and from talking to many doctors, I realised that medicine is DEFINITELY what I want to do.

Or you can say:

- There are a number of things that attracted me to medicine, but I think the main reasons would be the challenging nature, the interaction involved and the opportunity to make a positive and meaningful difference.
- You can mention a few of the above. The most important one is to mention the emotional and physical challenges.

12 MMI Work Experience: Team Working/Shadowing

How important is team working in medicine?
Or what did you learn from shadowing on the surgical wards?

I learnt:

- The importance of good teamwork e.g. I saw the surgeons, anaesthetists and nurses working together to manage a complex case in the operating theatre.
- It was very inspiring and gave me a great insight into the different roles played by the doctor, ranging from communication with the patient before operation, obtaining consent, explaining about the anaesthetic and keeping the patient involved at all times.

- It gave me an appreciation of how much teamwork is involved in operating theatre, and how important it is that every member of the team performs their role efficiently and effectively.
- Through my work experience, I learnt more about the resilience required to cope with relentless pressure and long hours.
- My observations in surgical theatre illustrated the dedication and pursuit of the medical team and the importance of combining medical knowledge, precision in procedures, good communication and interaction skills.
- In surgery, I was impressed how the doctors had good dexterity and had a keen eye for detail.
- In surgery, I was impressed by the surgeon's skill in using the latest technology to improve the efficiency of the procedure.
- Whilst attending ward rounds, I gained insight into the persistence and teamwork of the multi-disciplinary team to provide continuity of care and the compassion shown by the doctors in establishing a trusting rapport with patients.
- Listening to the patients talking about their condition, their experiences and how their lives was affected by their condition, has helped to improve my listening and communication skills.

13 MMI Work Experience: Patient's Culture

You said in your personal statement that the doctor understood the patient's culture. Give us an example.

- I realise that doctors need to understand not only the physiology of their patients, but also the cultural and social factors that influence the way they seek and receive medical treatment e.g. the doctor had to educate a diabetic patient on how to manage their condition during religious festivals such as Ramadan.
- I was struck by how sensitive doctors were to patients whose cultures are vastly different from their own and the need to be sensitive to those differences, in order to effectively help those patients.

14 MMI Work Experience: Shadowing a Cardiologist

What did you learn from shadowing the cardiologist?

- On the cardiology ward, what sort of tests were done? e.g. ECG, MRI scans, and cardiac ultrasound.

- Did you observe an angioplasty being done?
- Did you understand the reason for carrying out a coronary angioplasty?
- Did you see an aortic valve replacement? Why and how did they do it?
- What signs and symptoms did the patient present with?
- Did you get time to talk and listen to patients about their conditions, their experiences?
- How was their life affected by their condition?
- Did the doctor explain the results of their investigations with clarity and reassurance?

It is so important you that ask as many questions as possible during your work experience. If you are interested in studying medicine, you will look up these medical conditions and tests.

15 MMI Work Experience: Shadowing in A&E

What did you learn from shadowing in Accident and Emergency?

- In A&E, I was inspired by the way doctors worked under pressure in emergencies, by their good organisational skills and by their ability to priorities patients.
- The doctor had to be able to prioritise his work, and delegate his work to appropriate colleagues.
- In A&E, the doctor had to act under pressure,
- The doctor had to rapidly assess and prioritise patients, and recognise sick patients who require their immediate help.
- He coordinated the efforts of other members of the team.
- With effective communication, prioritising, delegating, and asking for help early, the team were able to work well for the good of the patient.
- I learnt the importance of a doctor being aware of his limitations and when to ask for help.
- I noticed how doctors must think critically to synthesize information, and to solve problems. They sometimes have to find out a diagnosis from a set of often unclear, ambiguous or contradictory facts or symptoms.
- I saw the excitement of stimulating work, the joy of helping patients and the challenge of interpreting studies.
- In A&E, the doctor dealt with angry and drunk patients and had to deal with a lot of self-inflicted problems.

16 MMI Work Experience: GP Practice

What did you learn from your work experience in the GP practice?

- The GP had a holistic approach to his patients. He looked after not only the clinical but also the psychological and social aspects.
- He dealt with varied patients from all ages, cultural and social background.
- He had the capacity to communicate effectively and sensitively with others, and the ability to discuss treatment options with patients in a way they understand.
- I was impressed by how the doctor modifies his behaviour to show respect, inspires confidence and motivates patients to implement whatever changes they need to make to positively affect their health.
- I also learnt the crucial role that communication plays in a GP's day. Not only did he have to explain complex conditions to patients who had no medical knowledge, he also acted as counsellor needing to show a lot of care, attention and empathy.
- I was impressed how GP communicated with patients of different backgrounds, as well as with colleagues who have varying depths of knowledge of medicine, and he used the appropriate level of jargon so that everyone understands.
- My work experience in a general practice highlighted the variety of people and the variety of illnesses seen every day, ranging from a sore throat to heart disease, and chronic illness. I gained an understanding of how the doctors are not only clinicians, but also counsellors and educators with the focus on medicine.
- Apart from treating patients he was involved in: Preventive medicine e.g. giving immunisations, educating patients about their conditions, managing and monitoring long-term conditions, managing his practice, running different clinics e.g. diabetic clinic.
- The way the GP treated his patients, giving the same degree of patience and kindness to every patient really impressed me, as did his impressive knowledge base.

17 MMI Work Experience: Challenges of Work Experience

What was challenging about your work experience?
What did you like most or least about your work experience?

Did the experience indicate that perhaps you were not cut out for medicine?

What new insights did you obtain?

What new skills did you obtain?

Describe one event that made a strong positive impression upon you.

Tell us about an interesting patient you saw during your work experience.

Will you really be able to cope with the emotional side of it all?

These are very common questions asked each year.

- I spent a lot of time talking to patients and relatives, and I feel proud of the beneficial effect I had on them.
- I loved the variety of work and the buzz of working in a team.
- I loved the idea of continuous learning and working in an intellectually challenging environment.
- What I liked least about my working experience in the hospice: a lot of patients did not have any visitors and they seemed very lonely.
- I observed the doctor giving bad news to a patient and I thought that would be a difficult thing to do.

18 MMI Work Experience: Holistic Medicine

What is holistic medicine and give me an example of when you saw holistic medicine during your work experience?

Holistic medicine means that you are treating people as a whole. You are looking after the physical, psychological, and the spiritual issues. Examples of holistic medicine include the following:

- When I worked in the GP practice, this elderly lady kept coming in complaining of headaches. When the doctor chatted to her a bit more he discovered she had buried her husband a few weeks ago and she was devastated. He referred her for bereavement counselling.
- Another patient had come in with a rash. Further questioning by the doctor revealed that she had lost her job a few months ago and was worried about her financial situation. Her rash was due to her stressful lifestyle. He referred her for counselling.
- A patient had been diagnosed with M.E. which could have significant impact on the patient and on the family. A severe form could prevent her from driving her car and she may be unable to work. The doctor

considered the psychological impact on the patient. He also had to consider the financial, social, and the impact on her husband and children. He referred her to social services.

19 MMI Work Experience: Useful Skills

What skills have you gained in your current work experience that are useful to medicine?

- What did you learn from your work experience?
- From my work experience, I developed awareness of the responsibilities, challenges, trials and tribulations of what it means to be a doctor.
- I have been exposed to patient care in the hospice.
- Working with different doctors has allowed me to witness a variety of styles and patient care interaction.
- Coordinating with doctors, nurses and others has given me an understanding of how integral teamwork and cooperation are to quality of patient care.
- During my work experience shadowing a doctor, I saw the excitement of stimulating work.
- The joy of helping patients and the physical and emotional challenges.
- My work experience also provided excellent opportunities for me to appreciate the importance of and further develop my own communication skills, increasing my self-awareness and building up my confidence as a team member.
- I also gained insights in how best to communicate with people suffering from disabilities, and patients who come from a different culture.
- I found the medical conditions very interesting and I went home and looked them up.

You must take the initiative and ask lots of questions.
- Why not ask patients what they think makes a good doctor? If you witness any procedures, talk to the patient about how it was for them.
- I attended classes for fourth year medical students and was able to observe the OSCE exams.
- The students had to diagnose problems from case studies. Having an analytical mind, I enjoyed observing their problem solving approach when they had to make a diagnosis based on an array of symptoms.
- After speaking to many doctors and medical students, I became aware

of the reality of medicine, the anti-social hours, the very long training process, and the challenges facing the NHS. This made me aware of the importance of time management, and to balance physical exercise and leisure with the academic workload.

- I spent just over three weeks shadowing a gynaecologist in hospital. I had the opportunity to visit many of the wards and clinics, attend theatre and watch a number of operations. My observations in surgical theatre illustrated the dedication of the medical team and the importance of combining medical knowledge, precision in procedures, good communication and interaction skills.

- Just talking to patients of different background has vastly improved my personal communication skills, my understanding of human nature and how to connect with people.

CHAPTER 11

MMI KNOWLEDGE STATION

The NHS is the government body that will be your future employer. You will be asked questions on its various bodies and functions.

In this chapter, we will look at questions that are specifically concerned with hospital life and the NHS. These questions are asked at both traditional and MMI interviews.

Examples of 20 MMI Knowledge questions and sample answers follow, and for ease of reference, they are listed in Annex 5 to this book.

1 <u>**MMI Knowledge Station: Barriers to Doctor/Patient Communication**</u>

What barriers are there to effective doctor patient communication?
Or what can hinder doctor-patient relationship?

You are relying on patients to tell you their symptoms. Patients may feel that they are wasting the doctor's valuable time. When patients are dishonest or withhold information, their treatment and even their life can be compromised. Some patients lie because:

- They are afraid of being judged.
- The examination room scares them.
- They are afraid of the diagnosis.
- They want to please the doctor.
- They omit details of their history which they deem unimportant.
- The patient may believe the doctor has not really listened to them and, therefore, does not have the information needed to make good treatment decisions.

It is important to tell the patient you are not going to judge their lifestyle or actions, and that you must know their complete medical history to make the correct diagnosis.

2 MMI Knowledge Station: Uncertainty in Medicine

In what way is there uncertainty in medicine?

- When patients are dishonest or withhold vital information, their treatment and even their life can be compromised. This would result in the proposed treatment not being entirely suitable.
- Pre-existing conditions which may interfere with the success of the treatment.
- Patients may not adhere to treatment for several reasons.
- The patient may develop unexpected complications that may have an adverse effect on the procedure.
- When a patient or relative says "How soon Doctor?", it is impossible to accurately predict such things as the likely quality of life and when death may occur.
- During surgery, the surgeon may discover some new problem or discover that the scale of the known problem is greater than predicted.
- Patients always want clear facts when weighing up the pros and cons of treatment. Doctors talk about percentage of risks but what that means for the individual patient is something the doctors do not know.
- We can never know in medicine how people will react to bad news. The patient may or may not already know about her grim prognosis. The patient may decide to make the most of her remaining time, or she could give up and sink into depression. Psychiatrists are never sure when they send a patient home from hospital, whether he will do harm to himself or to others.

3 MMI Knowledge Station: What is a diagnosis?

This was a very common question asked at medical school.

A diagnosis is the integration of information from various sources:
- A patient's signs and symptoms
- A full history
- A detailed examination
- Ordering appropriate tests and investigations
- When you get the test results, you will analyse all the information to establish a diagnosis and treatment plan.

4 **MMI Knowledge Station: Inequalities in Healthcare**

What does the phrase 'inequalities in healthcare' mean to you?

Trusts can make decisions on how to spend their budgets. This can mean treatment in one Trust may not be available in another Trust. The 'postcode lottery' means that individuals are receiving different levels of care depending on the region where they live e.g. some patients are turned down for expensive cancer treatment drugs and those a few streets away are allowed to have them. Parts of the population have a poorer understanding of their own health needs and do not always know where to go for help. They do not make use of the health services available to them in their area.

5 **MMI Knowledge Station: When would a doctor lie to a patient?**

A doctor would not lie to a patient. He may withhold telling the patient the truth. There are two main situations in which it is justified to withhold the truth from a patient:

- If the doctor had some compelling reason to think that disclosures would create a real and predictable harmful effect on the patient, it may be justified to withhold truthful information. This might include disclosure that would make a depressed patient actively suicidal.
- The second circumstance is when the patient states an informed preference not to be told the truth. Some patients might ask that the doctor instead consult the family.

In these cases, it is critical that the patient gives thought to the implications of abdicating their role in the decision making. If they chose to make an informed decision not be informed however, this preference should be respected.

6 **MMI Knowledge Station: Junior Doctors**

Some nurses in hospitals and GP practices are doing the role of junior doctors. How does this affect junior doctors?
- It reduces training opportunities for junior doctors, as specialist nurses carry out their work.

- This will affect the learning and progression of junior doctors as they have less clinical experience.
- The distribution of roles may help give junior doctors more time to relax and focus on their academics which could help them offer better care to patients and may also help them succeed in their exams.

7 MMI Knowledge Station: Factors affecting health or population

What are the factors that affect an individual's health or the health of the population?

- Smoking leads to asthma (lifestyle)
- Excessive drinking leads to liver cancer (lifestyle)
- Environmental pollution leads to lung cancer or COPD.
- Occupation: if an individual works in sewage work, then unhygienic conditions could lead to bacterial infections or illnesses such as Malaria.
- Country in which they live: in India tuberculosis is very common.
- Migration: if individuals come from a different country with a communicable diseases such as swine flu, then it could spread into the population.
- Obesity leads to diabetes, cardiovascular diseases, stroke, arthritis etc.

8 MMI Knowledge Station: History of Medicine

(a) What are the medical advancements over the last ten years that should receive a Nobel Prize?

Discoveries you may wish to include:

- Davinchi robot (robotic assisted surgery)
- HAART (highly active anti-retroviral therapy, the combination of the drugs given.
- PET scan and MRI (functional MRI)
- Stem Cell therapy
- Gene therapy

(b) How does medicine compare with 50 years ago?

Discoveries you may wish to include:

- Radiography has been complemented by the invention of MRI scanning for e,g. X-rays, CT scanning, ultrasounds,
- Vaccination has helped humans to control a large number of common diseases.
- Antibiotics have altered the management of common infections.
- The discovery of new HIV medication which have helped transform HIV/AIDS into a chronic disease. Specific drugs such as enfuvirtide which is an anti-HIV drug.
- Genetic testing of babies. Screening for serious genetic diseases in babies by sampling the DNA from cells either in the amniotic fluid sac or from the placenta, preventing babies being born with Spina Bifida or Downs' Syndrome.
- The invention of key-hole surgery which has further reduced the need for invasive surgery. This saves the NHS money as the patient spends less time in hospital as they recover quickly.
- Discovery of insulin that helps regulate the daily life of many diabetics.

(c) How does medicine nowadays compare with medicine 100 years ago? Can you tell us about something in the history of medicine that interests you?

Discoveries you may wish to include:
- Technology has led to a number of inventions, which means more accurate diagnosis e.g. MRI, X-rays, ultrasound, CT scanning, etc.
- The Internet has enabled doctors to share information and knowledge and has helped in the advance of medical research.
- The Internet has helped patients look up their own symptoms to try and diagnose themselves and question their doctor a lot more.
- 100 years ago patients did not tend to question their doctor as he was thought to be always right.
- The Internet has helped patients to gain information about a healthier lifestyle.
- Before the NHS was formed in 1948, patients had to pay for their treatment.
- Nowadays, the doctor's role has changed to more preventive medicine, education, teaching and management. Doctors now work more as part of a team than as a sole agent.
- A number of major discoveries over the past 100 years, e.g. vaccination and advanced knowledge of antibiotics, have helped to control and manage a number of common diseases.

- The introduction of the clinical governance framework helps to ensure that the quality of care provided by doctors is constantly monitored, improved, and maintained at a high standard.
- Genetic testing of babies. We screen for serious genetic diseases in babies by sampling the DNA from cells from the placenta or in the amniotic fluid.
- The discovery of the double helix structure by Crick and Watson in 1953.
- Stem cell research
- Sterile techniques in operations.
- The Royal College and the GMC have taken on a regulatory role and have improved clinical standards.
- Elderly people are living longer which has led to more diseases.
- The media play an important role in the NHS. There is an increased transparency, debating important health issues. This keeps doctors more alert.

9 MMI Knowledge Station: Becoming a Consultant

How old are you when you become a consultant?

Doctors complete a five or six year course at medical school, then two years as a foundation doctor, and then between six to eight years as a specialist trainee before becoming a consultant.

It is important you demonstrate knowledge of the medical training.

10 MMI Knowledge Station: Putting Someone off Medicine

If you were a career guidance teacher, how would you put someone off a career in medicine?

Highlight some of the difficulties and negatives about medicine.

11 MMI Knowledge Station: What are the 6 Core Values of the NHS?

1. Care
2. Compassion
3 Competence
4. Communication

5. Courage
6. Commitment

12 MMI Knowledge Station: Medical Treatments in Hospital or Community

Do the majority of medical treatments occur in the hospital or in the community?

In the community
- A lot of ill people will go to the local pharmacy to buy painkillers etc.
- A patient must go to his GP to be referred to a specialist.
- Many General Practices now carry out minor surgeries.
- A lot of patients with chronic disease will be monitored by the GP.
- The GP can be involved in preventive medicine e.g. immunization.

13 MMI Knowledge Station: Politics influencing Healthcare

How does politics influence healthcare decisions?

Politics influence healthcare decisions in several ways:
- Politics are important in setting the health care budget and determining the amount of available money to spend on the investigations and treatment of our patients.
- Some people in certain areas are restricted to what drugs and treatment they receive (e.g. postcode lottery).
- The budget is never sufficient for everyone. The demand always exceeds the supply.
- The European Working Time Directive has reduced the numbers of hours a doctor can work to 48 hours. This increases the need for more doctors and for nurses to do some of the doctors' roles.
- Governments may also take an active role in epidemics of disease, issuing vaccinations to vulnerable groups e.g. the measles outbreak in Wales in April 2013.
- By funding major campaigns for issues of importance and helping the NHS pass on messages to their patients e.g. the dangers of smoking and the fight against sexually transmitted diseases.
- Legislation is a political process. It sets the legal position for certain policies such as abortion, organ donation and stem cell research.
- Politics is also involved in funding for scientific research and can influence the development of new treatments for existing disease, which has a very real impact on the population at large.

14 **MMI Knowledge Station: NHS Problems**

What are the problems with the NHS?

The NHS has many issues:

- The biggest issue is adequate funding.
- Funding is always a limiting factor in medical treatment and at present the only source of funding is taxation.
- Long waiting time for operations, procedures and investigations
- Inefficiency issues, bed shortages, etc.
- The postcode lottery: If you have a disease that requires an expensive treatment, you may or may not receive that treatment, depending on where you live.
- The strains on the NHS resulting from the elderly living longer.
- The impact caused by the increased prevalence of obesity in UK.

15 **MMI Knowledge Station: Funding of Healthcare**

How should healthcare be funded?
Do you think it is right to allow private healthcare to run alongside the NHS?

Arguments in favour of private healthcare:
- Autonomy: If the patient can afford private health care, he should have the freedom and right to choose.
- If we did not have private health care, the NHS waiting list would increase drastically.
- Private patients pay National Insurance alongside their private medical care. This money can be used towards NHS patient's care.
- Some private hospitals send their patients to NHS hospitals to have scans, and pay the NHS.
- Some doctors do private work as well as NHS work. If they couldn't do so, they may choose to go abroad to work.
- GPs will be able to refer patients to both the public (NHS) and private health sector.
- If private healthcare was not available, patients may choose to go abroad for treatment, and come back to the UK with complications/side effects to be treated by NHS, and costing more money.

Arguments against private health care:
- When private hospitals send their patients to the NHS to have a scan, they are jumping the queue.
- In an emergency, NHS nurses and doctors will look after patients in the private wards in the NHS. This takes the nurses and doctors away from their NHS work and agency nurses may need to be hired, costing money.
- In private hospitals, doctors may be carrying out unnecessary tests to gain maximum money.
- There is a two-tier system, with only those able to afford private care having the choice to use it.

16 MMI Knowledge Station: Bariatric Surgery

Should obese patients be allowed Bariatric surgery on the NHS?

This is a very common question asked at medical school interviews. Weight loss surgery, also called bariatric surgery, is used as a last resort to treat people who are dangerously obese (carrying an abnormally excessive amount of body fat). This type of surgery is only available on the NHS to treat people with potentially life-threatening obesity when other treatments, such as lifestyle changes, have not worked. Potentially life-threatening obesity is defined as:
- having a body mass index (BMI) of 40 or above
- having a BMI of 35 or above, and having another serious health condition that could be improved if you lose weight, such as type 2 diabetes or high blood pressure.

For people who meet the above criteria, weight loss surgery has proved to be effective in significantly, and quickly, reducing excess body fat. However, it is always recommended that you try to lose weight through a healthy, calorie-controlled diet and increased exercise, before you consider weight loss surgery, as surgery carries a risk of complications and requires a significant change in lifestyle afterwards.

Because of these associated risks, most surgeons, whether they are working privately or for the NHS, would only consider a person for surgery if there was a clinical need, and not just for cosmetic reasons. Even if you are eligible for weight loss surgery, the demand for this surgery on the NHS is currently high. Therefore, there may be a considerable waiting list.

Weight loss surgery can achieve often impressive results in the amount of weight lost, but it should not be seen as a magic cure for obesity.

People who have had weight loss surgery will need to stick to a rigorous and lifelong plan afterwards, to avoid putting weight back on or to avoid long-term complications. This plan will include a carefully controlled diet and regular exercise.

The rapid weight loss may lead to unwanted loose folds of skin, which may need further surgery to correct.

Also, many people with mental health problems, such as depression or anxiety, find that these problems do not automatically improve because they have lost weight.

It is important to have realistic expectations about what life after weight loss surgery will be like.

Risks
As with all types of surgery, weight loss surgery carries the risk of complications, some of which are serious and potentially fatal, such as:
- Internal bleeding
- A blood clot inside the leg (deep vein thrombosis)
- A blood clot or other blockage inside the lungs (pulmonary embolism)

It is estimated that the risk of dying shortly after gastric band surgery is around 1 in 2000. A gastric bypass carries a higher risk of around 1 in 100. However, this risk can be as high as 1 in 40 if you have other risk factors such as high blood pressure or a BMI of 50 or over. As long as a person is willing and able to stick to their agreed plan afterwards, surgery can effectively reduce their weight and treat conditions associated with obesity, such as diabetes.

Recent research carried out in America found that on average:
- People with a gastric band will lose around half their excess body weight.
- People with a gastric bypass will lose around two-thirds of their excess body weight.

Both techniques also lead to a considerable improvement (and sometimes a complete cure) of obesity-related conditions, such as diabetes or high blood pressure. Primary care officials suggest people should try other options, such as fitness programmes and diet schemes before surgery is considered, as the procedures are risky and costly. This includes NHS Fit Fans scheme, which requires people to join a 12-week structured programme, and Why Weight? which offers nutritional advice and teaches cooking skills. The Live Well weight management service is an option for those denied surgery on the NHS, as well as "exercise on referral" which offers psychological support and focuses on exercise and nutrition.

Health officials said each weight-loss – bariatric – procedure costs the NHS between £8,000 and £10,000. In comparison, health officials said it costs £600 per person to complete Fit Fans and £600 per person for Live Well, with positive results achieved in both.

Requests for bariatric surgery should be considered on a case-by-case basis. The NHS should only fund the procedure where there is a proven clinical need and/or there are special circumstances which mean the patient is unable to lose weight in another way.

Bariatric surgery is just one approach to tackling the problem of obesity. GPs should refer patients to programmes in the first instance, in order to promote self-responsibility and the development of a long-lasting, more positive attitude to food and exercise for patients.

17 MMI Knowledge Station: Promoting Good Health

How can doctors promote good health, other than treating patients? Doctors can promote good health by:

- Discussing with patients their lifestyles. Advise them on healthy eating, encourage them to give up smoking, have safe sex, plenty of exercise, etc.
- Doctors can provide information and recommendations for support organizations such as Alcoholics Anonymous, Alnon, dieticians, and counsellors to help them to improve their lifestyle.
- Doctors can be involved in public health initiatives such as government campaigns, which can involve newspapers, radio and television.
- Raising awareness of mental illness and reducing the stigma associated with mental illness.
- Raising awareness of the obesity epidemic in the UK. Childhood obesity gives rise to increasing rates of diabetes later in life.
- Distributing leaflets and displaying posters in the GP surgery.

- Putting up posters and encouraging his patients to get involved in activities such as 'Race for Life' raising money and awareness for certain conditions.
- Giving immunization and educating patients about their condition.
- Screening programmes for breast cancer, cervical cancer and prostate cancer.
- Running family planning/sexual health and diabetic clinics.
- Increase accessibility to health care advice for lower socio-economic groups.
- Common health prevention messages may not find their way to the individuals concerned. For this reason, doctors should enhance health promotion targeting through appropriate media.
- They can provide interpreters for minority groups based on ethnicity with language barriers.
- To promote good health in the community, all available services must be used to their optimum by people in vulnerable groups.

18 MMI Knowledge Station: Change of Career Path

Why do some doctors change career path?

- They cannot deal with the intellectual, emotional and physical challenges of medicine.
- They do not like teaching, research, the long hours, the lack of resources and all the paperwork they have to complete.
- They may find it difficult to deal with death and to break bad news to a patient.
- Maybe they became too emotionally involved with patients.
- Perhaps they have health problems.
- Maybe they were pushed into undertaking a medical degree by their parents.

19 What is the Structure of the NHS?

The Department of Health controls the NHS. The NHS is divided into two sections: Primary and Secondary Care. GPs are the Primary Care who act as independent contractors to supply the NHS. The Health and Social Care Act 2012 aims are to put clinicians at the centre of commissioning, free up providers to innovate, empower patients and give a new focus to public life.

Secondary Care is care by hospitals and the A&E departments.

Tertiary Care consists of specialist departments in Teaching Hospitals and specialist hospitals (Great Ormond Street Children's Hospital).

For more information on the above look up healthhandcare.dh.gov.uk

20 What are the duties of a doctor?

GMC Guidelines 2013:

Knowledge, skills and performance
- Make the care of your patient your first concern.
- Provide a good standard of practice and care.
- Keep your professional knowledge and skills up to date.
- Recognise and work within the limits of your competence.

Safety and quality
- Take prompt action if you think that patient safety, dignity or comfort is being compromised.
- Protect and promote the health of patients and the public.

Communication, partnership and teamwork
- Treat patients as individuals and respect their dignity.
- Treat patients politely and considerately.
- Respect patients' right to confidentiality.
- Work in partnership with patients.
- Listen to, and respond to, their concerns and preferences.
- Give patients the information they want or need in a way they can understand.
- Respect patients' right to reach decisions with you about their treatment and care.
- Support patients in caring for themselves to improve and maintain their health.
- Work with colleagues in the ways that best serve patients' interests.

Maintaining trust
- Be honest and open and act with integrity.
- Never discriminate unfairly against patients or colleagues.
- Never abuse your patients' trust in you or the public's trust in the profession.

CHAPTER 12

MMI COMMUNICATION STATION

In this chapter are questions that are becoming increasingly frequent at MMI stations.

These questions enable interviewers to test your flexibility in dealing with difficult and sensitive issues. These role plays test insight, empathy, communication skills, honesty integrity and many more skills. **Examples of 6 MMI Communication questions and sample answers follow, and for ease of reference, they are listed in Annex 6 to this book.**

1   **MMI Communication Station: Train Crash**

You are a doctor walking past a train station.
You come across a train crash and you are the only doctor.
What would you do?

- Call the emergency services, and explain the scale of the accident so that they can put an Emergency Action Plan into action.
- Evaluate the situation, think about the available options and treatments and then take action.
- Make quick decisions about who to treat first, who can wait for treatment, and who is so severely injured that treatment is futile.
- Attend to those who need immediate treatment, and leave people with less serious injuries until the emergency services arrive.
- Check whether there are any doctors, nurses or first aiders who can help.
- When the emergency services arrive, notify them that you are a doctor and offer your assistance.
- Try to save as many lives as possible.
- Make split-second decisions about treatment, with no information about patient's history.
- Remain as calm and flexible as possible.

2 MMI Communication Station: Mistake leading to Patient Death

You are a junior doctor and you made a mistake and your patient died. What would you do? How would you feel?

- Speak to the consultant privately. Be open and honest. Tell him exactly what happened. Take responsibility for what happened.
- Do not discuss or explain to relatives how or why the error happened. The Consultant will talk to the relatives and the situation will be fully investigated.
- The investigation will uncover the factors and issues that led to the error and develop changes to prevent that error happening in the future.
- Document all evidence and results.
- Discuss the incident with the legal team.
- The crucial point is to identify why the patient died. Identify the problem and find areas for improvement.
- The hospital should introduce quality assurance programmes to increase patient's safety.
- These changes should be incorporated in the training and education of doctors.
- If the patient died because of a communication problem, the hospital should offer training to improve communication.
- Making such a mistake can be devastating for the patient, the family, the doctor and the NHS.
- Feelings of devastation, guilt and self–doubt should be addressed in counselling.

3 MMI Communication Station: Friend over Alcohol Limit

Your friend has just passed her finals as a doctor. She is out celebrating and gets very drunk. She goes to bed at 4 a.m. Next morning, she drives her brother to school, and the police stop her for erratic driving. She is over the alcohol limit for driving. It is her first offence and the police let her off. The hospital has two disciplinary teams. One just has a chat with students and tells them off. The other is much more serious and gives students a warning and puts it on their file.

Which team should she go to see and why?

She should go to the second team
- Even though the incident was isolated, it highlights many concerns. First of all, she risked her own life, her brother's life and the lives of other people.
- As a doctor, she would have known that the alcohol was still in her system and she was still under the influence of alcohol.
- She has worked in casualty and she is aware of the consequences of drunk driving.
- How do we know that this is the first time she has been drunk driving? Will she compromise patient care?
- It would be advisable to have some counselling.

4   MMI Communication Station: Rude Consultant

You are a third year medical student and the consultant is constantly rude to all the medical students in theatre. All week, he has been screaming at you for no obvious reason.

What would you do?

Medical students should not be expected to confront their superiors every time they encounter the questionable behaviour of a doctor.

- Do not confront the consultant in theatre in such a public manner.
- Speak in confidence with your tutor and report the consultant's behaviour, without suffering undue consequences.
- If the story is substantiated, the tutor should tell the consultant that students have witnessed inappropriate behaviour.
- Students and junior doctors, who are supervised by consultants, are very reluctant to report a consultant for inappropriate behaviour. They endure the bad behaviour.
- Policies and procedures are in place to assist aggrieved students.
- Medical Schools should provide an accessible and safe place for students to talk to someone about their options.
- Students often do not feel empowered to confront more senior doctors about unprofessional behaviour.

5 **MMI Communication Station: Telling a Patient Bad News**

How would you tell a patient they had 6 months to live?
Or how would you tell a patient bad news?

This is one of the most common questions asked at MMI and traditional interviews last year.

Many patients with cancer can recall in detail how their diagnosis was disclosed, even if they remember little of the conversation that followed. The doctor's competence in these situations is critical to establishing trust. Several approaches can be used to facilitate open communication with a patient.

Getting Started

- Before seeing the patient, get the facts right. Discuss the patient with the rest of the team.
- Ensure that you have all of the information beforehand so that you are adequately prepared.
- Turn off your bleep to ensure there are no interruptions.
- It is important to consider the setting in which to present such information.
- Gauge the level or amount of information the patient wants.
- The patients should be told all relevant aspects of their illness, including the nature of the illness itself, expected outcomes with a reasonable range of treatment, alternative risks and benefits of treatment and other information deemed relevant to the patient's needs.
- Set out the information in a clear and simple way, explaining any complicated issues in lay terms, and approaching difficult or potentially distressing issues about a patient's prognosis and care, with tact and sensitivity.
- Ensure the relatives have the opportunity to ask questions.
- Complete and truthful disclosure is important. Appropriate sensitivity to the patient's ability to digest complicated or bad news is important.
- Create a quiet, confidential setting and establish eye contact.
- Introduce yourself. Check patient's details. Ask the patient who else ought to be present, and let the patient decide.
- Let the patient know he can stop you at any time to ask questions or if it is all getting too much for them.

- Consider the holistic needs of the patient.
- Physical: Look at the treatment options.
- Psychological: What additional support can be provided e.g. support groups, Macmillan nurses, home help, etc.
- Social: what implications are there for the patient's work, lifestyle and family?

Find out how much the patient knows and what are his concerns.
- "What have you been told about your illness already"?
  or
- "You had some tests done last week. Do you know what the tests were for"?

You can begin to understand what the patient has already been told, how much he understands about what's been said and the patient's emotional state. ("I've been so worried I might have cancer that I haven't slept all week")

Find out how much the patient wants to know.
- It is useful to ask patients what level of detail you should cover.
- "Some patients want to cover every medical detail but other patients want only the big picture, what would you prefer"?
- Avoid jargon. Must be totally honest with the patient. Give the information in small chunks, and be sure to stop between each chunk to ask the patient if he or she understands.
- "I am going to stop for a minute to see if you have any questions"?
- Too much information can be overwhelming and confusing.
- If the patient starts to cry, wait for the patient to stop crying. If it seems appropriate, you can acknowledge it.
- "Let's just take a break now until you are ready to start again"
- You must be ready to deal with whatever comes up at a station.
- Offer the patient a glass of water or tissues.
- Do not try and stop the tears.
- Do not tell the patient to stay calm, or not to worry, or that everything will be ok.
- Give the patient all the options available to him. Explain what the next step would be, involving the patient in the choice.

Responding to the patient's feelings:
- Learning to identify and acknowledge a patient's reaction is something that is very important.

- "Could you tell me how you are feeling right now"?
- Let the patient know you heard and understood what he or she has said.
- Empathetic communication requires not only that we listen, watch, and understand, but, also that we reflect that understanding so that the patient knows it.
- We can reassure the patient that we will be present with them and there will be lots of pain relief as their disease progresses.
- Show attention with non-verbal cues, such as nodding. Allow silences while patients search for words.
- Acknowledge and legitimize feelings.
- Ask the patient if there are other areas of concerns.
- Conclude the conversation by reinforcing commitment to care for the patient and family, regardless of the decision they make.

Planning and follow-through.
- Synthesize the patient's concern and the medical issues into a concrete plan that can be carried out.
- Give the patient any relevant leaflets and information to take home.
- Make any appropriate referrals.
- Arrange to see him in clinic in two weeks.

6 **MMI Communication Station: Surgeon over the alcohol limit**

The neuro-surgeon had been out for dinner with his wife and had a few glasses of wine. His colleague called him in an emergency to operate on a complicated case.

What are the issues here?

The neuro-surgeon's ability to think clearly has most definitely been compromised by the alcohol. The neurosurgeon obviously thought he was sober enough to drive and operate. By getting into the car, he has broken the law for drinking driving. He could crash and injure someone. He could do serious harm to the patient. He would have been better to postpone the surgery or get another surgeon.

CHAPTER 13

EXAMPLE OF A TWELVE STATION MMI, WITH GUIDED ANSWERS

Station 1: Medicine

This station is designed to explore the candidate's background knowledge on, and motivation towards, medicine as a career. The intended purpose is to determine whether or not the candidate has prepared for the interview, by doing some background reading/research, and is designed to look into choices, decisions and interpretations, as opposed to a regurgitation of answers following coaching.

A number of questions appear on a computer screen and the candidate's answers will be used to aid the assessment. The interviewer will assess the applicant's suitability for a career in medicine and how they generally coped with the station. If the candidate exhausts the questions, the interviewer may chat to them in order to make his decisions, keeping to the areas outlined in the questions.

The interview will grade the candidate between 1 and 6 on the following:
- Ability in the topic area
- Communication skills
- Suitability for profession

Station 2: Logic (The Towers of Hanoi)

This station is designed to assess your logical thought processes and also your ability to give instructions clearly. You will be presented with a "puzzle", which you should try and complete. Once you have completed the puzzle, you will be expected to instruct the interviewer in completing the task as well. The object of the "game" is to transfer all the rings from the starting rod to the finishing rod. You can only move one ring at a time and you are not allowed to place a larger ring on top of a smaller ring. A pictorial representation of the puzzle is shown below.

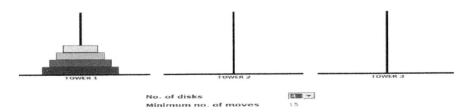

In addition to interpreting their ability to do the puzzle, the interview will watch your reactions and determine whether or not you display signs of frustration, aggression or defeatism. They will look for an ability to cope under pressure and a sense of humour, calmness or well-being, despite any frustrations. The candidate will be scored on ability to do the test and on ability to give instructions

Station 3: Problem Solving

This exercise tests your initiative and problem solving skills.

You are given a list of items that you would want to take in your suitcase for a two week holiday. You are told that you can only pack half of the items available. You need to consider some of the following issues:

- How long is the trip?
- If you are going for two weeks, you will need a lot more than if you were going for a long weekend.
- What is your destination?
- If you are going to a civilized place, you will be able to buy stuff and maybe cheaper.
- What activities are planned?
- Are there any cultural requirements that need to be respected?
- If you are going to the jungle, you will not need electrical items.
- If you are going to visit friends or family, you can borrow stuff from them. Do they have a washing machine, or is there a launderette or river nearby?
- Are some items more of a luxury e.g. perfumes and make up.
- If you have friends going with you, can you share some of their items?
- In all prioritization exercises, there may be several possible correct answers.

- Once you have eliminated the luxury items, you must be able to justify your choices between the others.

Station 4: Tolerance and Ethics

This station has been developed to look at professionalism, tolerance and, to a degree, ethical views of the candidate and reflects perceptions in what are seen as important areas. The interviewer may ask you to talk about the "rights" and "wrongs" associated with the questions, based on your answers, and in defence of your answer. If the interview feels that you are finding the discussion/questions hard, he may use the time to find out how you feel about and what you understand by professionalism.

Station 5: Team Work

You are presented with the following scenario: You are on a day out in London with a group of friends. One member of your group, who has never been to London before, becomes separated from the rest of the group in the Underground. What actions would you take?

This question tests your initiative and resilience, as well as your team working skills. For example:
- It is important for everyone to get back to base safely.
- Dividing tasks amongst team members.
- Applying insight into teamwork and leadership.

This station is designed to explore your ability to problem solve and deal with a crises. Clearly there is a need to plan a strategy and hopefully a successful outcome. Have a team meeting to discuss what can be done and allocate tasks:
- One person should go back to the hotel.
- One person can go on the street to get a signal so they can call the friend's mobile phone.
- One person can travel on to the next station in case he has gone ahead.
- Call his home to tell his family where to meet us at a certain time.
- Arrange for everyone to meet back at the hotel at a certain time to decide what to do if the friend is not found.
- Call the police.

Station 6: Communication

You are requested to instruct the examiner to draw a picture of a household object, in a way that they will then be able to identify it, or
- Without using your hands, explain how to tie your shoelace.
- Without using your hands, explain how to wrap a Christmas present.

You may be asked to describe a picture to the examiner. If the picture is a scene, focus on what is happening rather than describing background information. The picture may be a series of geometrical shapes, which you have to describe to another, who will attempt to reproduce it using your description.

These are rather complicated exercises which students find very difficult to do. This station is designed to test the following skills:
- Being able to break down the task into a series of small steps.
- This tests your ability to listen and understand instructions.
- Your ability to give clear, unambiguous instructions.
- Your instructions need to be specific.
- Being able to communicate to different age groups. Explaining to a 6-year-old boy will be different to facing a 40-year-old man. Your tone of voice and body language will be very important here.
- Tell them to feel free to interrupt you, if there is something they do not understand.
- Try not to make your answer too complex. Keep it as simple as possible.
- If they have a very confused look on their face, clarify with them that they understand what you are saying.
- You might have to do it all over again.

Station 7: Role Play Communication: Dealing with Bad News

This station has been designed to see how you deal with breaking bad news. You are to imagine that you have:
- Accidentally run over your neighbour's cat whilst reversing your car. The cat is badly injured, but it does not look like it will die or need to be "put down". The cat is in the back of your car and you are going to take it to the vet. You have five minutes to break the bad news to her.
- Or you have been looking after your neighbour's rabbit while she was on holiday and it escaped.

This station is designed to see how the candidate deals with and relates to breaking bad news. This role-play tests insight, communication skills, honesty, integrity, trustworthiness and empathy along with their reaction to the scenario.

- You need to recognize the reality of the scenario. Some students laugh when given this scenario and treat it as a joke. This will not help you to get in! You will be expected to take responsibility for the mistake (i.e. not blaming the cat for being in the wrong place at the wrong time) as well as showing empathy and recognising the pain that may be caused.
- You should be able to deal with the neighbour's emotional response, be it anger or grief. If they start crying, do not try and stop them from crying.
- You should not be too defensive in your apology, nor should you be over justifying what has happened. Do not tell the neighbour that you understand what they are going through, because you do not.
- You should, at the very least, offer to help regarding the cat's condition: run her to the vet, pay the bill, offer to do chores, do the gardening, or drive her to the shops etc.
- You will be assessed, not only your ability to deal with the situation, but also on your tone of voice and body language, as well as what you actually say. You will be scored by the observer and the role player independently. The observer can, if necessary, get involved by making sure that the scenario is fully played out, and that an outcome is agreed. Whether deemed satisfactory or not is dependent on the candidates answers.

Station 8: Creativity, innovation and imagination.

This station will look into your creativity and imagination. The scenario that will be explored by the assessor is the following:
You are holding a dinner party for three guests. These guests can be any three people (alive or dead). Who would you invite and why? The dinner party is to have a medical/dental theme. How would you make it memorable?

Choice of Guests
Guidance: there may be any number of reasons but the assessor may try to get you to explore areas of choice, mix of guests, common themes, what they would talk about. As host, there must be some reasons as to why they have been chosen and this should be explored. You must give some degree of reasoning for your choices.

What sort of food would you provide?

Guidance: Again there may be any number of answers and the assessor will try to explore these, i.e. what you would do if you found out one of the guests was vegetarian.

How would you make the dinner memorable?

Guidance: Some suggestions might be having to dress as a doctor/dentist, using dental/theatre instruments to eat the food with, serving mouthwash rather than champagne, etc.

Students hate this type of question. You may want to invite President Obama and Nelson Mandela for dinner. There are several questions you may wish to ask them:

- Who influenced them when they were young?
- What drove them to do the things they did?
- Who did they most admire?
- What are their regrets in life?
- What would they like to ask each other?

Station 9: Reasoning and explanation.

This station is designed to assess your reasoning and explanation skills. You are given a list of people, which details their age and occupation. There is about to be a nuclear attack and only you and five others will fit into the nuclear shelter. You have been elected as the leader and all the people on the list trust your decisions implicitly; they will not question your choices and are aware that only you have the authority to make a decision. You will be asked by the interviewer to explain whom would you choose and why. You have to make choices, and are not allowed to choose or select people based on random selection methods, such as drawing straws or names from a hat etc. Additionally, what other information would you also like to have been provided with to help with your decision?

Mary Brown	Female	21	Mechanic
Noreen King	Female	82	Cook
Nell Gleeson	Female	30	Housewife
Mary Murphy	Female	40	Doctor
Tom King	Male	31	Barber
Mark Dunne	Male	35	Investment banker
Mary Egan	Female	12	Schoolgirl
Tom Gleeson	Male	32	Computer engineer

John Cleary	Male	40	Carpenter
Robin Jones	Male	60	Retired headmaster
Bert Curtin	Male	24	Nurse
Sinead Talty	Female	50	Policewoman
Steven Jones	Male	59	Farmer
Betty O'Connor	Female	23	Pregnant first time mother

In reality, there are no right or wrong answers. They are basically exploring the candidate's ability in reasoning, in problem solving, in rational thinking and to explain their choices. They are looking for candidates who appear to have sound reasoning ability and an idea of how to clearly put forward their thoughts.

Question: Which five people did you choose? Explain why you made the choices. The interviewer is exploring your decision-making. Note there is a married couple on the list, nuclear war will cause sterility of the soil, and no "machinery" will work if an electromagnetic pulse has been used. What value / skills does each person bring? What additional information would you like to know, before making your choices?

Answers: There are many issues to be considered. For example:
- Survival of the group in the long term.
- You need capable, fit healthy intelligent people.
- The need for reproduction.
- Spread of skills e.g. mechanic, doctor, carpenter, etc.
- Elderly and people with severe disabilities would not be chosen.
- People with suitable occupations for the future would be chosen.
- People's physical and mental health, marital status, and relationship to each other e.g. Mr and Mrs Gleeson are husband and wife, and they may not wish to be separated.

Station 10: Personal Insight

You are asked to imagine you are half way through your first year of medical school. Each year, the school has a peer professionalism assessment programme that requires six of your classmates to assess you. You also do a self- assessment. The results of your performance, along with the class average, are presented below.

You are asked to discuss your results with your interviewer; you may wish to consider the following when looking at the data: What would you consider as the overall presentation? Are there any "problem" areas? What other information might you seek to guide your professional development?

Scoring ranges from low = 1, through neutral = 3, to high = 5

Behaviour	Score by self	Score by peers	Class average (N=80)
Takes on extra work willingly to help out colleagues	5.0	4.8	4.8
Encourages communication and collaboration among colleagues	4.0	4.5	4.5
Manages conflict in a respectful manner	4.0	3.5	4.5
Displays appropriate empathy towards patients	4.0	3.8	4.8
Listens and responds to others receptively	5.0	2.5	4.2
Acknowledges limits of own knowledge or ability	5.0	3.4	4.6

This station is designed to help explore personal insight through the medium of self-reflection. While the data contained in the table may not necessarily be reflective of the actual applicant, it should raise a number of points which should be explored by the assessor, who will assess you on your overall presentation? The assessor will look at whether there are any problems, i.e. with reference to an over inflated ego, or how the student views himself.

Question: What other information might you seek to guide your professional development? Possible answer: the views of staff or other people who work with me.

Question: How would you create an action plan so that next year's results will be better? Possible answer: Attempt to be more sensitive to the perceptions of others, acknowledge that perhaps the views of others are valuable and that I do not necessarily know it all.

Question: How will you monitor your performance to ensure that you are making progress? Possible answer: Seek the views of the group in a year's time as well as ask informally.

Question: Do you have any additional comments before we end this discussion?

Station 11: Dealing with a Dilemma

This station is designed to explore the applicant's ability to problem solve a successful outcome.

You are presented with a scenario in which you and three friends are on a day trip to Paris. You have a couple of hours to spare before you all have to get the train back to London, and you all decide to take the Metro, from Gare de L'est to travel to Porte Dauphine, to visit a Museum. One of your friends (who is an Insulin dependent diabetic) becomes separated from the group in the Metro.

What actions would you take to find your friend?

Neither you nor your friends can speak French, and your lost friend does not have a mobile phone.

Clearly there is a need to plan a strategy, and hopefully a successful outcome. There are a number of things to bear in mind:

- The friend does not have a mobile phone but there is nothing to say the remainder of the group do not.
- The medical emergency nature needs to be appreciated, for the outcome to be realised.
- It is suggested that one person would go to the museum, and another to the point of departure, in case the lost friend goes there, but clearly all entrances may not be covered,
- The local authorities would need to be informed (perhaps someone can speak English and assist),
- There needs to be a plan on meeting or making contact at a certain time, in order to decide what to do if the friend is not found by the time the train is due to return to London,
- Go to the local hospital in case he has gone into a coma and been admitted.
- Call home in case he rings and tells his family where to meet us at a certain time.
- Call the British Embassy in case he goes there.

Station 12: Data Interpretation

You are informed that, in Birmingham, fluoride is added to the water, but this is not done in Cardiff. A study was conducted to assess the association between fluoride and dental caries. Children in Cardiff and Birmingham were examined and data collected. The data are shown in the table below. The proportion of 7-year-olds with no dental caries (no fillings or teeth extracted) in Cardiff and Birmingham are shown divided by social class: non-manual professions, and manual professions of parents.

	Manual	Non-manual	Overall
Cardiff data (n=50)	40%	25%	35%
Birmingham data (n=50)	25%	15%	20%

You are asked to answer and discuss the following questions:
- Do you think a total sample of 100 children is enough data to give reliable estimates for the whole of Cardiff and Birmingham?
- Why should we examine the same number in each area?
- What do the overall figures tell you about the relationship between water fluoridation and dental caries?
- What do the data, divided by social class, tell you about the relationship between water fluoridation and dental caries in Cardiff and Birmingham?
- What do the data tell you about the effect of fluoridation on health inequality?

Some of the above information was taken from Cardiff University.

CHAPTER 14

APPLYING TO MEDICAL SCHOOL

Competition to get into medical school is intense. You need to be realistic about your admission chances. There are many qualified applicants who will not be accepted.

Apply to medical schools of varying degrees of competitiveness. You should not take the risk of applying only to the most competitive schools. The outcome may be rejection by all of them.

All UK medical schools have similar non-academic requirements: work experience, teamwork, communication skills, leadership, responsibility and contribution to university life. You must be prepared to be able to speak enthusiastically about why you want to go to their medical school. They are looking to see whether, if they made you an offer, you would actually accept it. The best way to answer this question is figure out the university's strengths, and why they appeal to you.

Check out the relevant University website, research the course, and examine what it is you are looking for in a university.

It is vital that you visit the medical school on open day. Open days are an invaluable opportunity to see the university and medical school, and meet current medical students, and ask them questions. Medical schools want to know why you want to go to their medical school.

Indicate the reasons for your specific interest in their medical school. They want to know you researched their school, by visiting the website, talking with current medical students and graduates, and reading published material.

The following factors should all be considered when deciding to which of the medical schools you will apply:

- Get a feel for the university.
- Do you feel comfortable with the locality in which the medical school is set?
- It is important to consider the recreational and cultural attractions in the area.
- Some medical schools use cadavers, others use computer-generated imagery for their sessions.
- Is the school in a big city or a small town?
- What activities are available outside of the school?
- London is very expensive compared to other locations.
- Do you want an intercalated degree? At UCL and Imperial College, the course is six years.
- Does the medical school have early patient contact?
- Does it have hospital placements abroad?
- Elective – this is a period of time, usually between 4-8 weeks, where you can undertake a placement of your choice, usually abroad.
- What are the living expenses?
- Do you need a car, or is the public transport good?
- Do you wish to stay living near home, or do you wish to experience living in another part of the UK?
- Do you want to see a different patient demographic e.g. large cities may see a wider variety of patients, possibly with more ethnic diversity?
- Do you want a large teaching hospital?
- There may be particular facilities that have attracted you to the medical school.
- Would you prefer to study at a campus, or a city-based medical school?
- Does it have an international reputation?
- What are the medical school's unique features?
- What do you know about the course?
- Why do you think it will suit you personally?

Medical schools now vary dramatically in their educational styles, with some schools relying heavily on student-driven learning, while others take a more traditional lecture-based approach.

Medical schools are quite proud of their individual curriculum and teaching style. It is essential that you spend time and effort choosing your medical school. In developing your list of medical schools during your application process, consider which format best suits your learning style.

Do you need the structure of large classroom lectures, or are you better in small, creative, well-directed groups?

You should familiarize yourself with the distinction between traditional, problem based learning (PBL), and integrated courses.

Traditional medical school: Traditional style involves lectures, tutorials, essay writing and research. They want their students to have a good grounding in these areas, as a solid foundation on which clinical practice can be built.

PBL: Involves working in small groups and it encourages the students to direct their own study.

Integrated Medical School: Striking a balance between traditional learning and PBL style.

The Application

All medical schools in the UK require three A grades or 1A*AA. Most of them require minimum 5 A* at GCSE. Some do not allow you to re-sit your modules and some do not allow you to re-apply to their medical school.

Students are allowed to apply to only four medical schools, even though the UCAS application form has five boxes to tick.

A medical school cannot tell to where else you applied. However, the BMAT is only required for Brighton & Sussex, Lancaster, Leeds, Oxbridge, UCL and Imperial College. It is important not to apply to all BMAT universities, in case you do badly in the BMAT test. If you sit the BMAT, note that UCL will have a copy of your essay and, months later, will ask you questions on it at the interview. So, make notes immediately after your BMAT test, and think about how you could improve on your essay.

It is a good idea, as an insurance policy, to choose two medical schools with lower grade requirements.

With some medical schools, you need to check what is their UKCAT score cut-off point. Normally, you will have already received your score before submitting the application form.

Make sure you fit the criteria, otherwise your application will be discarded from the admission process.

Medical schools often try to determine not only the best applicants, but also the best applicants who they think will accept their offer. Make sure you convince the medical school you are very keen to attend their school.

In addition to the basic medical course, it is also possible at some medical schools, to gain an intercalated degree. This is an additional bachelor's degree in a subject of interest taken during an extra year.

Nottingham students graduate with a combined degree, BMedSci, within the 5-year-programme.

At King's College and Queens Mary's, the majority of students do the intercalated degree. At Imperial College London and UCL, it is compulsory.

Preparing for medical school

Ideally, your preparation should begin at least two years before you submit your application.
Many students who are rejected are extremely strong candidates and would make excellent doctors. So, the competition for places is fierce.

Typically, a medical school receives 2,000 - 4,000 UCAS applications. They will call only 25 percent for interview, rejecting the other 75 percent.

To reach the interview stage, you will need top grades at GCSE, AS and A-level. You will also need an excellent Personal Statement.

Many medical schools do not consider repeat applicants, and some do not accept repeats in exams. So check in advance.

Why do you think Problem Based Learning (PBL) would suit you?

- I am a goal-oriented, organized and enthusiastic person and I study well on my own. I also find it interesting to study in small groups. For Biology at school, we had to do course work as a group. We were all given different sections to do and we had one week to prepare. At the end of the week we met to present our sections and I found that very exciting.

- I like the fact that PBL provides a practical approach to medicine.
- I have always enjoyed finding out information by myself and in that sense the PBL approach with its supervised small group structure is ideal.
- During my A levels, I organized a small study group with a couple of my friends so that we could learn together and utilize our time more effectively.
- As part of our school project which I had to undertake with other students in my class, we had to negotiate who was the most appropriate students to prepare different sections of the work. At the end of the week, we had to present it to the class.
- As part of our Biology society, which I set up, we would plan a different topic to discuss each week. We would go away and look up the topic independently and meet up every Wednesday after school and present our findings to the group.
- I like the idea of learning from each other in a small team. This is less intimidating and promotes team spirit.
- I am focused, enthusiastic and organized and I think these qualities will enable me to make a good contribution to my team.

Why do you think traditional teaching would suit you?

This is the method that I am used to and which I have found successful in the past. I always find attending lessons or lectures the first step of learning as it gives me background of the subject, and I can go to the library and find out more.

What are the advantages and disadvantages of PBL?

Advantages
- PBL involves learning from materials surrounding a clinical case that is self-directed by the students.
- I feel it would be well suited to those who are motivated and show initiative. The small groups in PBL would probably make students feel more at ease about asking questions.
- Students have freedom to practice time-management.
- Part of the PBL learning environment is teaching the others in the group about what you have learnt.
- Small groups allow for team building skills and more individual involvement.

- Early exposure to real life scenarios can be of great beneficence.

Disadvantages
- PBL can sometimes be thought to leave gaps in medical student's learning.
- At the end of the year, students may be at different levels and in some areas some students will have very good understanding and knowledge and other students may have very little.
- Some students in a group may be unmotivated and disrupt others in the team.
- Some students may want to work at a faster pace than others within a group. This could lead to some students being held back, and possible conflict within groups.

What are the advantages and disadvantages of traditional teaching?

Advantages
- Traditional teaching tends to have more structure in comparison to other methods of teaching. This helps to ensure that all students receive the same information. Students receive a sound knowledge base and background understanding before dealing with patients.

Disadvantages
- The course may not suit people who prefer less structure and more self-learning.
- Students may find they are having difficulty keeping up or may be frustrated, as they do not feel challenged.
- Sometimes, initially, there can be little contact with patients. Some students may find it uninspiring to sit in a lecture theatre all day.
- Within a large group, students may not have the courage to ask questions.

Integrated course
- I like the idea of an integrated course. This combines the combination of the independent learning of the PBL and the structure of traditional.

CHAPTER 15

PERSONAL STATEMENT

For medical school, you must submit a Personal Statement with your UCAS application.

Too many applicants do not put sufficient time and effort into preparing their Personal Statement. You will not be called for interview if your Personal Statement is not impressive.

The process of preparing a Personal Statement really begins on the day you decide you may want to apply to do medicine.

Keep a written record of anything that may be useful to help you write your Personal Statement. Read articles on current affairs, especially on NHS problems and ethical issues.

Get involved in a broad variety of activities. Become a member of sports teams, join clubs and societies at school, work in a nursing home or hospice for a few hours each week, raise funds for charity, talk to medical students who may be past pupils or friends of your older siblings or friends. Ideally, you will have been doing these activities for more than a year before you submit your Personal Statement with your UCAS application.

You must demonstrate that you are someone who is caring, compassionate, committed, has good communication skills, and has an independent mind and an adventurous spirit.

The application process is like chess game: to achieve success, requires foresight, strategy and dedication.

A Personal Statement usually includes sections on education, relevant work experience, community services, volunteering, clubs, publications and hobbies.

You must be honest in your Personal Statement. It should include:

- Why you want to study medicine.
- Your awareness of the reality of being a doctor.
- What you gained from your work-experience.
- Don't emphasise locations or how eminent is the consultant. The medical school are only interested in what you learnt from your work experience. Be specific e.g. mention the patient's condition, the treatment, and the impact on the patient. Demonstrate empathy to the patient.
- Whatever your passion or hobbies, always relate it back to how the skills you have learnt will help you in a medical career.
- Refer to skills you acquired or improved: working in a team, leadership skills, communication skills, coping with stress or challenging behaviour, compassion and empathy.
- Admissions also want to know that you are a sociable, well-rounded person who knows how to relax and de-stress, and what you will offer to university life e.g. join the rowing team, football team, drama society etc.
- It is important to demonstrate a well-balanced lifestyle e.g. academic, sport, music, friends etc. I am a rugby player and have represented my school, club and country in competitions, and I am looking forward to competing at college level in the UK.
- Although daunting, the Personal Statement is also an exciting opportunity to impress the selection team.
- Creating a memorable Personal Statement cannot be completed in one setting.
- You should set aside at least four weeks to write the statement. Expect to go through about 20 drafts.
- Be sure to allow time for a teacher to give comments. After the third draft, it is time to give it to someone for expert opinion
- Choose two or three people with experience in writing/reading Personal Statements and gather their thoughts on aspects, content, grammar and flow.
- Do not ask too many people for opinions, but do ask people who are qualified / experienced to comment.
- Think outside the box about what sets you apart from other candidates.
- Admissions are looking for good people with a host of good attributes.
- Read your Personal Statement out loud to check the content and flow.
- Don't include anything you can't talk about at the interview.

- Show commitment and dedication e.g. long standing effort in a particular academic or sport activity, regular attendance at a society or club, or helping out every week at a hospice.
- Starting your own society or group at school can also be a great way to acquire leadership skills and demonstrate initiative e.g. biology society. Each student could read an article each week and present it to the group.
- Comment on how your work experience confirms your decision to study medicine.

CHAPTER 16

INTERNATIONAL STUDENTS

All of the information in this book is relevant to International Students. You will apply through UCAS, submitting a Personal Statement, and hopefully be called to a Multi Mini Interview (MMI) or Traditional Interview depending on which medical school you apply to.

It is advisable, as it is for UK applicants, to get your English Language teacher to check over the Application Form and Personal Statement, before submitting them.

The number of places available at each medical school to international students is restricted, and so competition is fierce.

Some students have already gone through the lengthy process of getting sponsorship by their government. It is important that you let the medical school know that you are an international applicant, and also whether or not you have sponsorship from your Government.

This section focuses only on questions that are specific to international students, but you must read the whole book because it applies to all students.

Why study medicine in UK?

- Why do you want to study medicine in the UK, and not in your home country?
- Studying in UK away from home could be challenging. What are these challenges and how would you cope with them?
- How are you going to cope with the UK weather?
- What are the differences between NHS health care and the system in your country?
- This is your first time away from home. How are you going to cope?
- In what ways are you an independent person?

- Most patients in UK do not pay for their health care. Do you think this is good or bad?
- What do you think of the NHS?
- How do you think working in a GP practice in the UK differs to that in your country?
- What can you bring to the medical school?
- How will you deal with cultural differences in UK?
- How will you cope with communicating in English to patients and others?

Some additional typical interview questions:

- Tell us about the research you did.
- Has your experience in the real world helped you improve your interpersonal skills? If so, how?
- Why are you applying to study medicine now, and not when you did your A Levels?
- When did you change your mind?
- How will you feel studying alongside younger students?
- How will you handle the temptations attached to student life?
- How will you adjust to challenges in medicine?

CHAPTER 17

GRADUATE/POSTGRADUATE ENTRY

Many postgraduates apply for the five year medical school courses. However, there are few places available, and the competition for places is fierce.

Places are awarded to postgraduates who have good degrees, normally a first or 2.1, combined with good work experience. A 2.2 class degree is normally not sufficient. At Multi Mini Interviews (MMI), you will be asked similar questions to those for undergraduates.

Carefully go through each prospectus, look at the websites, go to open days and a get a feel for the Medical School. Some of the courses are run entirely separately for the four years, while others integrate at different times. Course structures will vary so you need to read the prospectuses carefully. It is vital to go to open days, and to speak to other medical students.

Some medical schools will not reconsider an application from a candidate who has been previously rejected. Others will see reapplying as commitment to medicine. Check with each medical school to make sure you meet their requirements. GAMSAT is required by several of the medical schools.

There are some possible potential advantages to doing medicine as a post-graduate. You will hopefully be older and wiser than your classmates, who have come straight from school. You will have been out in the real world.

The perspectives you gain from working in the real world, with real people, are invaluable in providing understanding and compassionate care to whatever area of medicine you practice. You should reflect on your employment, work experience or voluntary work, and how it has helped you. Also, consider what other transferrable skills you learned during your degree?

By applying as a postgraduate, you demonstrate your commitment to doing medicine. Postgraduates and mature students are more likely to be committed to medicine, and less likely to drop out.

Many postgraduate courses offer patient contact at the early stage, which is an advantage. One disadvantage of entering medicine as a postgraduate is the extremely busy workload at the medical school and hospitals, with less time to have a part-time job outside.

You can bring a breadth of experiences and valuable life skills to the medical school and medical profession.

Questions Specific to Postgraduates

- Tell us about your research project
- Have your experiences since school helped you improve your interpersonal skills? If so, how?
- Why are you studying medicine now and not when you did your A Levels?
- When did you change your mind?
- What can you bring to the medical school?
- How will you feel studying alongside younger students?
- How will you adjust to the challenges in medical school and later as a doctor?

CHAPTER 18

UKCAT AND BMAT WITH 19 PRACTICE ESSAYS

Biomedical Admissions Test (BMAT)

Students applying to study medicine at Brighton & Sussex, Lancaster, Leeds, Cambridge, Imperial College London, Oxford and UCL are required to sit the BioMedical Admissions Test (BMAT). You **must** practice for the BMAT and the UKCAT.

The test, which takes place in September and November, consists of three sections:

1. Aptitude and skills (60 minutes-35 multiple-choice or short answer questions)
2. Scientific knowledge and applications (30 minutes-27 multiple choice or short-answer questions)
3. Writing task (30 minutes-one from a choice of three short essay questions)

Practice Essay Titles:

'Our zeal to make things work better will not be our anthem: it will be our epitaph.' What do you think is meant by this statement? Give examples supporting and disproving the statement.

'Medicine is an art form rather than a scientific discipline.' Do you agree with this statement? In what ways could medicine be considered an art form, and in what ways could it be considered a scientific discipline?

'Stop moaning! The pain is there to help you!' What does this statement imply? Give examples that illustrate how pain can be beneficial and others that illustrate the opposite. How can you explain the differences in the function of pain?

'A cost to an individual can be justified by a benefit to the group.' Do you agree with this hypothesis? Outline an argument in support of, and in opposition to this statement. What factors influence the rights of an individual over that of a group?

'In the scientific world, advancements can only be made if mistakes are allowed to happen.' Explain what you think is meant by this statement. Can scientific advancements be made without mistakes being made first? What do you think determines whether a scientific outcome is a mistake or advancement?

'The main benefit of patient consent is that it relieves doctors of blame for bad decisions.' Write a unified essay in which you address the following: Explain the argument underlying this statement. What are conventionally regarded as the benefits of patient consent? Give an example of a situation in which a patient's consent would be meaningful, and another in which it would not. How should clinical decisions be made?

'Higher education and greater numbers - that is a contradiction in terms.' Write a unified essay in which you address the following: Expand the argument underlying this assertion. What do you understand by 'higher education'? Is it qualitatively different from other types of education? Present an argument that it is, in fact, possible to provide higher education for the majority of the population.

'Merit and equality; they are incompatible' Write an essay in which you discuss your understanding of this statement. Do you think this statement is true?

'Is medicine an Art or Science?' Write a unified essay in which you address the following: Explain why medicine could be considered an art, and in other situations may be considered a science, giving examples from your own experiences.

'You can only believe what you know is true.' Write a unified essay in which you address your understanding of the statement, giving examples of when this statement would be true or others when it would not be.

'There is always a conflict between religion and science.' Do you agree with this statement? Why would religion and science conflict? Outline an argument for this statement, and also against this statement, giving examples of a situation where there would be conflict, and another in which they could work together.

'Doctors should always maintain patient confidentiality.' Write a unified essay in which you address the following: explain the argument underlying this statement. Why is confidentiality important? In what situation would it be possible to break confidentiality and why?

'Doctors learn to be good doctors from practising on the wards, not from books.' Write a unified essay in which you discuss this statement, explaining the benefits and disadvantages of both methods of learning.

'Patients with self-inflicted illness should not be treated on the NHS.' Write a unified essay in which you address the following: what is your understanding of a self-inflicted illness? Present an argument for this statement, and also against this statement, giving examples.

'Natural selection no longer applies in the 21st century.' Do you agree with this statement? When would natural selection still apply? And how does modern medicine affect it?

'Genes control our lives.' Write a unified essay in which you discuss how genes can affect our lives, and also how other factors may be more important than our genes.

For the BMAT essay it's very important to practice doing essays in the timed thirty minute periods.

Immediately after doing the BMAT, write down everything you wrote in your essay. At the UCL interview they have a copy of your BMAT essay and they will ask you what you thought of your essay and how you could have improved on it.

Write down how you could have improved it. This will give you points to discuss at the interview.

UKCAT Test for Medicine and Dentistry

If you are doing the UKCAT, you should also practice the HPAT papers which are sat in Ireland, and the GAMSAT papers which are sat in Australia.

Students who sat the UKCAT found that the more practice they had on timed IQ-type tests, the better prepared they felt. You can buy books that contain practice questions of a similar type to the UKCAT.

The medical schools use the test scores in different ways: Some will specify a minimum mark; others will use the score alongside all of the other entrance criteria as an extra piece of evidence.

If you reapply for medicine, you have to resit the UKCAT.

More information can be found at www.ukcat.ac.uk.

CHAPTER 19

EXAMPLES OF INTERVIEW QUESTIONS AT INDIVIDUAL UK MEDICAL SCHOOLS
(based on information provided by interviewees and the medical schools)

A lot of research and information has been gathered regarding the contents of the interviews at individual UK medical schools. The questions asked include questions from more than one candidate, so there are far more questions listed than you would expect to be asked at a single interview. It is not possible, because of lack of space, to include all the questions asked at each medical school and the tips about each school. If you would like to contact us, we can provide that information.

Aberdeen Medical School

The University of Aberdeen uses the multiple mini interview (MMI). There are seven stations, each taking seven minutes to complete. Candidates are scored in each of the following areas:
- Ability to express ideas freely and coherently
- How well they use their existing knowledge to formulate answers to unknown areas
- Their ability to follow a reasoned argument and to formulate an opinion
- The degree to which they are prepared for questions
- Their ability to discuss different aspects (advantages & disadvantages) of a problem/situation
- The degree of motivation, commitment, reflection and sensitivity demonstrated

Station 1
- This station is about your passion and desire to do medicine.

- Pros and cons of medicine.
- Why do so many people want to do medicine?
- How can you tell if someone really wants to do medicine?
- Name 5 of the most important qualities a doctor should have.

Station 2

- Personal statement - essentially a discussion on work experience. What did you learn from your work experience? Each work experience is discussed briefly. Which is the one you learned most from? What area of Medicine would you like to go into? What are the differences for city and rural doctors? How will patients, cases and treatments differ? What about small, isolated communities - what issues may there be regarding confidentiality? How does professionalism play a role here? How many years does it take to become a GP? How many to become a consultant? What are the stages of registration with the GMC? What do you do as a junior doctor? How do FY1 and FY2 years differ?

Station 3

- Why Aberdeen?
- What do you like most and least about the course here?
- What is the course structure here?
- What will you be doing here over the next 5 years?
- There are lots of questions on their course.

Station 4

- What is professionalism?
- Discuss the importance of professionalism.
- Lots of questions on confidentiality
- Name 5 of the most important qualities a doctor should have.
- How have you shown these qualities?
- What are your strengths and weaknesses?
- Why is it so important for doctors to be professional?
- Give an example of a time a doctor showed an important quality, and why was it needed in the situation.

Station 5

- What have you read recently in the news?
- Tell me about an article on medicine/research you have read recently. General discussion on the issues discussed in the article and other critical thinking questions.

Station 6: Team Player/Team Leader
- Give an example of teamwork and leadership from your work experience.
- What is a multidisciplinary team?
- Give an example of a time when you were part of a team that didn't work well. What went wrong and what would you do differently next time?
- What are the most important features of teamwork? What are the qualities of a good team player?
- Loads of questions on teamwork and leadership.

Station 7: Role Play
- A girl has a broken her arm. Ask her how it is impacting her daily life and find out about her accident.
- An epileptic friend wants to drive. Speak to her.
- Talk to a patient who has a stroke and is living alone at home.
- Would you tell someone you had given them the wrong drug, if it wouldn't have a negative impact on their health and they would not otherwise find out?
- A fellow medical student is having problems. You have to find out what are his issues, discuss them and help him. He is struggling with his studies.
- What would you do if a medical colleague arrived half an hour late to work, and he smells of alcohol?
- What would you do if a patient sends you a friend request?
- Discrimination and dealing with problems on wards. You are a junior doctor. You are upset because you get all the boring jobs, whereas other junior doctors get more interesting cases. Why might this happen, and what would you do?
- As a junior doctor, you talk to a patient who isn't following doctor's advice on changing their lifestyle choices.

Anglia Ruskin Medical School

They have Multiple Mini Interviews (MMIs), which are designed to gain further insight into your personal qualities and cognitive skills. They are comprised of a series of 10 mini- interviews, each lasting 7 minutes with a brief rest between each station. The interviews consist of scenarios and tasks, which will be typically assessing:

- Interpersonal and communication skills, including empathy
- Teamwork and leadership
- Preparation and motivation
- Critical thinking, problem solving,
- Ethical / moral reasoning
- Integrity

What are the differences between a GP and a hospital doctor? Questions about my volunteering and whom I met, where it was, how long I was there, and what I learnt from it.

What are the qualities of a good doctor? Why study medicine?

At another station, a question on whether it is better to spend more money training new doctors, or on recruiting doctors from other countries.

At the next station, I had to give instructions to a man to pick up blocks and small balls, but he couldn't see them.

At another station, I had to speak to a first year medical student. She was staying out late at night, and coming drunk to lectures. She was stressed with the workload and didn't want to go to dissections. She hasn't spoken to her family in ages and misses her mum.

Talk to a man who continually forgets to take his medication. Find out more about him, and help him.

At the next station, I was asked lots of detailed questions about my Personal Statement.

At another station, I had to instruct a person to place different paper shapes in a particular order, but I was not allowed to see what they were doing. Towards the end, I was asked what I did well and not so well and how would I improve.

Here, I was asked about a doctor who keeps prescribing Homeopathic Medicine. Is that bad? If so, why? How may it affect the NHS, and what if anything should fellow doctors do about this doctor who is easy going and prescribes anything?

At this station, I had to choose 2 out of 4 items to discuss with a single mother about her child. The mother swears in front of the child, the child is not at school, the child watches adult shows, and there is broken glass on the floor. I was asked to explain my priority.

Here, I had to choose whether to invest in a stroke facility or in diabetes prevention. Some Information was given. I had to explain my choice.

At another station, as a medical student, I had to talk to an old man. He had been looking online at the symptoms of illnesses. He compared his symptoms to those online, and was convinced he had a serious illness. He was depressed and began to cry. His dog had recently died.

Here, I had to make a choice about how to allocate funds in Mozambique. Either use the funds to prevent malaria, or to train doctors from the country to perform better anesthetics because surgeries there are unsafe.

At another station, there were lots of questions on teamwork and leadership.

Aston Medical School

Aston Medical School curriculum was developed by Leicester Medical School. Aston medicine interviews will include 7 to 10 MMI Stations. See Leicester Medical School for the questions.

They look for:
- Oral and written communication skills
- Listening skills
- Empathy, compassion, respect and dignity
- Emotional intelligence
- Problem solving
- Motivation
- Team working
- Being able to lead as well as follow
- Knowing your limitations and knowing when to ask for help.

Birmingham Medical School

University of Birmingham states that the best candidates will demonstrate:
- *Motivation for medicine*
- *Communication*
- *Empathy*
- *Self-insight*
- *Ethical reasoning*
- *Data interpretation*
- *Ability to evaluate information*

The seven stations are as follows:

- **Ethics:**
  Students will be given an ethical dilemma and asked to describe how they would go about solving the problem using the 4 ethical principles of medicine

- **Motivation and Insight into Medicine: (Challenges faced by practitioners)**
  Students will be asked to discuss the difficulties that a doctor faces today. They ask lots of questions on your work experience

- **Data Interpretation:**
  The student will be given some data relating to a doctor/patient scenario, and asked to interpret this data in relation to the particular scenario they are given.

- **Interpretive Task: (Engagement with a student)**
  At this station, the student will be asked to have a short conversation with a 4th or 5th-year medical student.
  This station is primarily designed to assess the student's communication skills, especially in situations where they are meeting someone totally new.

- **Motivation and Insight into Medicine: Personal qualities**
  Here the student will be asked about their work experience in medicine, and what they have learned about people working professionally in this field.

- **Dealing with Personal and Ethical Challenges:**
  The student will be given a difficult doctor/patient scenario and will be assessed on their personal qualities in their response, and their insight into how they deal with an ethical dilemma

- **Interactive Task: Role play**
  At this station, the student will be given a situation and a role to assume prior to the interview, which will take place with an actor. Typically the actor takes on the role of a patient, and the student takes on the role of a doctor with something difficult to explain to them, or bad news to tell them. This assesses the student's communication, professionalism, and compassion in a much more realistic way.

Station 1 This was a debate station in which you had to decide the best out of 4 potential recipients for a liver transplant. The four patients were:
- Prisoner
- Few weeks old Infant
- Middle aged man with a family to care for
- An ex-alcoholic

Station 2 A £10 fee for GP services. Give arguments for and against.

Station 3 Explain a change in inhaler dosage to a patient. Discuss the uncertainty in diagnoses. What would you do if you prescribed the wrong dosage and discuss methods to prevent this.

Station 4 Ask a 3rd year medical student about the university.

Station 5 Insight into medicine and NHS/ personal challenges in medicine.

Station 6 Dosage maths question: calculate the dose of drug, relative to patient weight, to wear off after a certain time.

Station 7 Self-evaluation: if you make a mistake, how would you cope, and what can be done to prevent it.

Brighton and Sussex Medical School

Multiple Mini Interviews (MMI) will consist of five discussions, each lasting ten minutes, with a minute between each discussion.

Applicants will move from each discussion in turn, until they have completed a full circuit – this will take 54 minutes.

One station has lots of questions on teamwork, leadership and work experience:
- Talk about a time you used your leadership skills.
- Do you prefer teaching or doing clinical work?
- What did you learn during your work experience?
- When have you made a mistake?
- What skills do you have?

At another station:
- What do you understand about the role of a doctor?
- What would you do if you were in charge of NHS funding in Brighton?
- Who make up Brighton's homeless community?
- What kinds of people will you interact with in Brighton?
- Many homeless people come to hospital for a place to stay. How do you deal with this?
- You have to teach 13-year-olds in a deprived area. What would you teach them?
- Why do you think BSMS send medical students to educate others?

A station on the 6 Core Values of the NHS:
- Care, Compassion, Competence, Communication, Courage, and Commitment.
- Why do NHS core values exist?
- Which value do you think is your strength?
- When would a doctor not be compassionate towards a patient?

A station on the NHS
- You have to spend money on 2 areas in NHS. Where would you invest?
- The elderly population is increasing. Should NHS introduce euthanasia or restrict the number of children per family?
- Taking into consideration the elderly population increasing, where would you increase funding in the NHS?
- Why is the elderly population a burden to the NHS?

Bristol Medical School

Stations: 10
Time at each station: Five minutes
Time in between stations: One minute

1) Teamwork: with reference to extracurricular and work experience, you are asked about the importance of teamwork and leadership and how you have acquired these skills.

2) Bristol Medical School: questions about the Bristol medical course specifically and about how medicine is taught I.e. Lectures, clinical, pre-clinical, intercalation, traditional vs PBL). You are asked to spell out what happens in each year of study (including intercalation). You are also required to know about Bristol, the city.

3) Practical station: a table of surgical equipment, gloves and trays are put in front of you with a long list of instructions. By following the instructions, you have to correctly cut and dispose of a surgical needle and thread - correct use of instructions and diagrams are crucial. Important not to rush this task

4) Maths: a number of very wordy tasks that only required basic multiplication and division, with questions in a medical context. Not difficult, but pressurised.

5) Instruction / Description task: a photo of a portion of a person's face is given with a blank piece of paper and a list of instructions. You have to describe a facial anomaly, determine whether the person is male or female, state their age, and sign and date the page

6) Scenario: Firstly, you are asked to define informed consent. You are then given a number of medical scenarios and asked how you, as a doctor, would approach them. You are asked how you would communicate to a person who is deaf, and how you would deal with a patient who has dementia.

7) Role play: you are given a brief to read (in the break between stations) which describes the scenario.
A patient is due to have an operation, and I had to convince her to give

up smoking as it may cause complications during surgery. Midway through, she reveals that her operation is to remove a cancerous tumour.

8) Motivation to study medicine: Why I would make a good doctor? Discuss the last article I read. What is wrong with the NHS?

9) Work experience/ Voluntary Work: What I learnt from it? What are the challenges of medicine, etc.?

10) Non-academic interests: What I do out of school? What I learn from it? How are out of school activities applicable to medicine etc.

Buckingham Medical School
(This is a private medical school)

There are between ten and twelve stations, each lasting seven minutes, and they normally include, but not necessarily be restricted to:
1) Tests of ability to communicate and empathise with simulated patients simulating complex life histories.
2) Tests of capacity to reflect upon the applicant's own life events, which may include those described in their 'personal statement'
3) Structured questioning on comprehension task
4) Tests of numerical skills relating to common tasks in the practice of medicine
5) Tests of ability to observe and summarise information from a video recorded interview between a doctor and a simulated patient
6) Tests of ability to identify strengths and weaknesses of communication skills exhibited during a simulated consultation between doctor and patient
7) Tests of ability to follow instructions for a practical task involving physical interaction with a simulated patient, and of capacity to interact sensitively and safely with the patient when undertaking the task.
8) Tests of ability to communicate and work collaboratively with colleagues through set collaborative tasks.
9) Tests of capacity to establish partnership with individuals through negotiation.

Station 1
- Video: A doctor with a patient. Comment on the doctor performance: good, fair or poor?
- Talk about the doctor's body language.
- What did he not do well? What were his weaknesses?

Station 2
- Theme: teamwork (role play)
- Talk to a 30- year-old man who has a slight disability. Help him put together a Lego car following instructions cards. One of the cards is missing and he was gets very upset and frustrated.
- You have to calm him down. Afterwards, you are asked what strategies did you use? Is teamwork important?
- Why is teamwork important in medicine?
- How did you find working with the patient?
- What techniques were used?
- How would you improve?
- Why would teamwork be important in a hospital setting?

Station 3
- What do you know about zika virus?
- Should doctors go on strike?
- What is the biggest mistake you've made?

Station 4
- What are the Issues about doctors using social media?
- Here are some pictures of a medical student's profile. Would you report this student?
- Will you change your opinion if the photos were posted before he was a medical student?

Station 5
- Calculations without a calculator:
  - You are given a graph relating to medication dosage and the height and weight of the babies.
  - You have to work out the weight and the height, and calculate the dose of the medication she should be given.

Station 6

- Role play: Talk to a person. Ask questions to find out more about him. You discover he is a teacher who went to prison for hitting a student.

Station 7

- Theme: observation skills
- You are shown a video of a doctor and patient. Afterwards, you are asked questions on the consultation.
- What was the patient's primary complaint? What were the associated symptoms? What is the patient's occupation and social set up? How long has he been in pain? Where is the pain, and what medication is he on?

Station 8

- This is a prioritisation station.
- You have to prioritise, in order of importance, a list of duties to be performed by a GP's receptionist.
- You then have to talk to the receptionist, who is not happy, and discuss why you have changed the prioritization.

Station 9

- Apart from medical use, how else could you use rubber gloves?
- How important is convergent and divergent thinking in diagnosis?

Station 10

- Examiner gives you various scenarios.
- And you can respond with 1 or more options below:
  1. Do nothing
  2. Discuss with other staff
  3. Get advice from a senior member of staff
  4. Report to the professional body
- Typical scenarios: doctor taking a bribe, doctor not washing his hands before surgery, doctor smelling of alcohol.

Cardiff Medical School

Applicants will rotate around 9 stations in turn. Each station will last 8 minutes. The interviews focus on exploring the personal qualities and attributes important in developing good doctors in the future.

The attributes include:
- Medical motivation and awareness of the career
- Caring ethos and a sense of social awareness
- Sense of responsibility
- Evidence of a balanced approach to life
- Evidence of self-directed learning and extracurricular activities
- Referee's report

There is a rest station, so you get a break half way though.

Station 1
C21 Course:
- What is your understanding about the C21 course?
- How are you suited for this course?
- Why do you like the C21 course? When have you used self -directed learning and what challenge did you face from it?
- Why do you want to study at Cardiff, in particular? How are you able to contribute to Cardiff as a student and a potential student ambassador? Will there be any difficulties you think you will face at Cardiff? Why not study closer to your home?
- What is the difference between Welsh NHS and English NHS?
- C21 has early patient contact with the GP. How does this change through the rest of the 5 years?
- Tell me about harmonisation in the 5th year.
- What challenges do blind people face?
- As a GP, how would you deal with a blind patient?

Station 2
Insight into medicine:
- Understanding of what medicine is.
- What can you bring (experience or knowledge) to medicine? Why do you want to be a doctor rather than a nurse?
- What makes a good doctor? What are the qualities that doctors should have? What is a doctor's role in confidentiality of a patient?

Station 3
- A patient, with cancer, is refusing life saving treatment.
- What are the ethical issues here?
- Is autonomy more important than beneficence?
- What are your views on organ opt-out?

- What are the GMC guidelines?
- In what way is a doctor professional?
- When were you in a team. Tell me about a problem you faced, and how you overcame it.
- What skills do you need as a team leader?
- There are lots of questions on team player and team leader.

Station 4

- Define empathy.
- Explain a situation when you showed empathy.
- A patient who is due a hip replacement has been left for over 100 days on the waiting list.
- How would she feel?
- How would you deal with stress?
- Why do doctors get stressed?

Station 5

- Question 1: Here is a picture of rural Wales. Describe what you see?
- https://cdn2.recombu.com/media/digital/news/legacy/M10809/1347893290_w670_h458.png à it was basically the picture given.
- What are the possible problems associated with providing health care in rural areas? How can you improve it?

Station 6

(This station was a paper and pen task, so no verbal involvement)
I was given a picture of a swollen hand, and asked to describe it on paper.

You are given two pictures of Wales, one picture was Cardiff harbour; the other was a marathon through the city. Referring to these pictures, discuss the benefits and challenges of working here in the NHS. (Perhaps discuss: large population, transport links, easy communication, nearby hospitals, multicultural and diverse, leisure facilities, etc.)

I was given 3 calculation questions. (no calculator allowed)
1. A dosage question
2. A percentage question
3. A graph question
- Why is numeracy important in a doctor's job?

Station 7

- To lose weight, an obese patient wants a gastric band operation but is reluctant to exercise or diet? What would you advise or do in this situation, as a health care professional?
- Who suffer discrimination? (Ageing population, obese people, people who smoke, or drink, etc.)
- Tell us your views on assisted suicide. Should it be made legal?
- What are the advantages and disadvantages of it?
- What are the ethical issues?
- You are given a picture of an elderly man on a ventilator. Describe how it affects him, and what challenges he faces.
- What are the ethical problems of prescribing unconventional medicine?
- What are the qualities of a good team member, and what challenges have you experienced working in a team?
- What are the ethical problems of using E-cigarettes?

Station 8

- What is good and bad about the media?
- What activities do you do outside of studies, and how do you cope with stress?
- Medicine is stressful. How will you cope?
- What are the challenges of working in a team?
- Tell us about a problem you faced, and how you overcame it.
- What skills do you need as a team leader?
- When have you worked in a team?
- How important is teamwork in medicine?
- What makes a good team?
- What was your greatest challenge in a team?
- What did you learn from it?
- What would you do differently?
- Tell me about a stressful situation, and what you learnt from it?

Station 9

- You are given two pictures of rural Wales: one is very green land and the other barren. Describe the pictures individually and compare them.
- Tell us about the placements we have here at this medical school.
- To where and when do we send you on hospital placements?
- When do you work in rural areas?
- Tell us your views on assisted suicide.

- Should it be made legal?
- What are the advantages and disadvantages of it?
- What are the ethical issues?
- What are the qualities of a good leader?
- What are the advantages and disadvantages of medicine as a career?

Dundee Medical School

There is a mandatory MMI interview consisting of ten 7 minute stations. Each station assesses the applicant based on three criteria:
- Content and substance of the interviewee's response
- Communication
- Global assessment of suitability for medicine.

The domains covered by the station are:
- Communication and empathy, teamwork, preparation for medical school, critical thinking, ethics, fairness, respect, personal statement, integrity check and community involvement
- Students can expect questions about their understanding of a medical career, the curriculum at Dundee and current medical issues in the press, including ethical topics.

At one station:
- Why do you want to come here?
- Tell us about our course.
- Why medicine?
- What have you done to prepare you for medicine?
- What are the negative aspects of our course?

At another station:
- What did you learn from your work experience that influenced you to do medicine?
- What are the demands of medicine?
- What is empathy and how important is it?
- When did you show empathy during your work experience?
- What surprised you during your work experience?

At another station:
- Questions all about Was teamwork and leadership.
- When have you worked in a good team, and when have you worked in a bad team?
- How important is teamwork in medicine?
- What are your qualities?
- What are the qualities of a good doctor?
- What is professionalism?
- What are the duties of a doctor?

Another station:
- This has an ethical scenario:
- You are a doctor in A&E. A seven-year-old boy needs an urgent blood transfusion. If he doesn't have it, he will die.
- However, his parents refuse to give consent. What would you do?

Another Station:
- You are a doctor on duty. You notice that your medical colleague, who is also your friend, smells of alcohol and is acting strangely.
- What would you do?

Another station:
- This is on research. What research have you done?
- What research is going on here in Dundee Medical School?
- How important is research in medicine?

Another Station:
- What interesting articles have you read recently?
- When have you showed good communication skills?
- How important is communication in medicine?
- During your work experience, when did you see a doctor communicate well?
- What are your weaknesses?

Another Station:
- You are given paper cut into various shapes. You have to explain to another person how to match the shapes with a board of shapes without you touching or pointing to the shapes. You realize the person doesn't understand terms like circle, triangle, rectangle etc.

Another station:

- What is GMC, and what do they do? There were questions on cheating at medical school. You see a fellow medical student, who is also your friend, cheating in an exam. What, if anything, would you do? Or someone you know is using their sister's coursework as their own. What would you do?

Another station:

- Should hospital car parks be free to everyone, or only to some people? Who should pay: staff, patients, visitors, the elderly, disabled etc.?
- You are given a list of gifts. You have to decide which gifts a doctor could accept from patients. You have to put them in categories ranging from acceptable to totally unacceptable.
- I had to guide a man, who is blindfolded, to use tongs to pick up and put down Lego men in various locations. There were various obstacles in the way.

Another station:

- You are asked to discuss 'whistle blowing'. You are then given various situations, and asked how you would react.
- For example, you see your medical colleague, who is also your friend, about to drive home under the influence of alcohol after a night out. What would you do?
- You are asked what are appropriate sanctions against medical students who do one of the following for example: sign in for another student into lectures or clinics; are seen cheating in an exam; are copying someone's coursework; are under the influence of alcohol on ward duty etc. The interviewer read out a list of offences, and a list of possible punishments. You then talk about your choices.
- You are asked to discuss issues arising from a language barrier.
- For example, you are given a shuffled pack of playing cards. You ask the patient, who has learning difficulties, to sort the cards into some of the following say: hearts, spades, diamonds, clubs, odd numbers, even numbers etc.

Edge Hill Medical School

They have Mini Multiple Interviews (MMI), which will assess the following;

- Understanding and motivation for wanting to join the medical school at Edge Hill University;
- Verbal communication skills;
- Integrity / probity;
- Teamwork / leadership;
- Empathy and compassion;
- Awareness of current health challenges;
- Ethical awareness;
- Awareness of self and others;
- Prioritisation / decision making;
- Interpretation of data.
- **The University of Liverpool will act as their contingency. See Liverpool MMI for questions.**

Edinburgh Medical School

Edinburgh Medical School use an MMI interview style.

The MMI interview have been designed to test the following:

Motivation to study medicine and genuine interest in the medical profession
- Insight into your own strengths and weaknesses
- The ability to reflect on your own work
- Personal organisation
- Academic ability
- Problem solving
- Dealing with uncertainty
- Manage risk and deal effectively with problems. Statement on the core values and attributes needed to study medicine
- Ability to take responsibility for your own actions
- Conscientiousness
- Insight into your own health
- Effective communication, including reading, writing, listening and speaking
- Teamwork
- Ability to treat people with respect
- Resilience and the ability to deal with difficult situations
- Empathy and the ability to care for others
- Honesty

The structure of the day will involve four stations. Each station will be scored separately by two selectors, marking independently.

Exeter Medical School

Exeter Medical School uses Multiple Mini Interviews (MMI) to determine whether applicants possess the non-academic qualities they are looking for:

- Good communication skills,
- Evidence of reflectiveness (insight into their own strengths and weakness)
- Decision-making skills
- Teamwork skills
- Evidence of the empathy required to become a successful doctor.

There are seven stations, each lasting five minutes, generally with three questions per station.

Room 1:

- You are a junior doctor on your first week of A & E. You are with a 15-year-old patient who is having a miscarriage. Her mother storms into A & E demanding to know what is going on. The girl doesn't want her mother to know she is pregnant because things are bad at home: her younger brother has leukemia, and she does not get on with her step dad, or brother, anymore.
- What are the issues?
- As a junior doctor, what would you do in this situation?
- How would you deal with the mother?
- The mother is abusing you and saying how awful you are for not letting her see her child. How would you feel?
- Leukemia is a big issue and can cause lots of stress. What is the possible effect of the boy's illness on the family?

Room 2:

- Clipboard simply says: "Stress. You will be discussing stress".
- First question: "How does stress present?"
- Question 2: "How do you know when you are stressed? Give me a specific example of when you were stressed.
- Why do doctors get stressed?

Room 3:
- Qualities of a Doctor:
- Question 1: "What qualities does a doctor need?"
- Question 2: "What qualities do you have that will make you suitable to be a doctor?

Room 4:
- Why do you want to study medicine at Exeter?
- Why does PBL suit you?
- What experience do you have of independent learning?
- What can go wrong with PBL?
- What would you do if someone isn't pulling their weight in a team?
- Why do you prefer PBL to more traditional learning?
- What was your greatest challenge?
- What did you learn from it?
- What are you most proud of?
- What did you like most and least during your work experience?
- What did you learn from your work experience?

Room 5:
- Question 1: What is a common complaint about the NHS
- Question 2: " Tell me about a specific newspaper article you have recently read which relates specifically to the NHS"
- Question 3: "Tell me about another specific newspaper article you have recently read, again specifically to do with the NHS

Room 6:
Ethics
- You are a junior doctor in A & E. An 8-year-old girl needs an urgent blood transfusion to stay alive, but her mother doesn't want her daughter to have the transfusion. What would you do?
- A grandmother has just been diagnosed with advanced cancer. Her daughter, who is looking after her, doesn't want the grandmother to know she has cancer. What are the issues here?

Room 7:
- "What is your greatest achievement?"
- What is empathy?
- Give us an example of when you showed empathy during your work experience.

- Give us an example when you saw holistic medicine during your work experience.
- How important is communication in medicine?

Glasgow Medical School

The interview session will last around 30 minutes. There are two interview panels (A and B), with two interviewers on each panel.

The interview has two main parts:

Personal Statement and Typical Medical School Questions (12-15 minutes): Generally, this part of the interview allows you to dictate which parts of your personal statement you would like to showcase. Make sure you can discuss the curriculum in-depth, and also be able to discuss current issues affecting both Scotland and the rest of the UK.

Problem-solving, in a Scenario Setting (12-15 minutes): You will be given the option to select one of two scenarios prior to the interview. You will discuss the issues around the scenario with the panel.
- Revisit your personal statement (interviewers have no knowledge about you other than your name).
- Think of examples of your achievements and skills.
- Consider your personal characteristics.
- Reflect on previous interactions or experiences.
- Explore what being a doctor means, and the related themes or topics around this.
- Scenario: (There can be a choice of three).
  For example: Should an alcoholic be allowed a liver transplant before he has given up alcohol?
- Why medicine?
- Why Glasgow?
- Is Glasgow your number one choice?
- What aspects of the course appeals to you?
- So what happens after you have your medicine degree? For hospital doctors? For GPs?
- What age are you by the time you're a consultant or a GP?
- If you had £10billion, what would you do with it to improve the NHS?

- What are the issues concerning junior doctors working 40 hours a week?
- What are the different aspects of communication?

Other students were asked:
- Why have you chosen us?
- What do you know about our course?
- What are the advantages and disadvantages of PBL?
- What can go wrong in a team?
- What would you do if someone does not pull their weight in a team?
- Why is teamwork so important in medicine?
- What did you enjoy most about your work experience?
- What did you do in the nursing home?
- What are the problems with elderly people living longer?
- What are the problems with the NHS?
- Tell us about a time when you were in a position of responsibility.
- There are lots of questions on the personal statement and on work experience.
- What is the difference between the English NHS and the Scottish NHS?
- What are your qualities?
- Why should we take you rather than someone else?
- Should we go for the Opt-Out system for organ donation?
- What are advantages and disadvantages of the Soft-Opt-Out system?
- Tell us about your work experience. What was challenging about it?
- What are the challenges of medicine?
- Why not choose another caring profession?
- What did you like most and least about your work experience?
- There was a lot of questions on team player / team leader
- What can go wrong in a team?
- What are the demands of medicine?
- What is empathy?
- How important is empathy?
- When did you show empathy during your work experience?
- What surprised you during your work experience?

Hull and York Medical School

Hull and York's MMI format varies greatly from other medical schools in that it has four different tasks

Two mini-interviews (10 minutes each, and 20 points each)
- You will have two personal interviews, each with two interviewers.
- You will be asked two questions during each of these mini-interviews and interviewers may ask you to expand upon your responses.

One mini-interview will focus on:
- Your understanding of current issues in medicine
- Why you want to be a doctor
- Insight into, and motivation for a medical career

The other mini-interview will focus on:
- Your critical thinking skills
- Your personal qualities such as empathy, tolerance of ambiguity and resilience

Scenario station (20 points)
- 5 minutes
- In the scenario, we want to find out how you react and respond in a given situation. Outside the interview room, you will have two minutes to read a short introduction about the scenario.
- An actor and an assessor will be in the room.
- The actor will be playing a character, and you will need to interact with that person in the same way as you would in real life.

Group discussion (20 points)
- 20 Minutes
- The main aim of this group activity is to allow the assessors to understand how well you can work within a group or team. They are interested in your ability to work collaboratively with a group of peers, how well you contribute relevant information to a group discussion, and if you can articulate your own thoughts effectively and clearly in this setting.
- There will also be a senior Hull York Medical School student participating in the process and acting as scribe, participating in the discussion, and capturing your ideas. In addition, there will be another

assessor in the room who will not participate in the discussion but he will complete ratings for each student.

Task station (20 points)
- 5 Minutes
- You will be asked to perform a task and either scored on the result or on the way your approach the task.

During the whole MMI, we will be observing and scoring you in the following areas:
- Your ability to work collaboratively in a group
- How you contribute relevant information to the group discussion
- How effectively and clearly you articulate your own thoughts in a group setting
- Insight into a medical career
- Your understanding of the values in the **NHS Constitution**
- Motivation for a medical career
- Your awareness and understanding of current medical issues
- Your communication skills
- Your understanding of and motivation for the Hull York Medical School MB BS course
- Your personal qualities such as empathy, tolerance of ambiguity and resilience
- Your ability to think critically
  - A discussion about how to help a lady on a plane who is scared of flying.
  - A discussion on what a GP should do when a patient, who keeps requesting morphine, is suspected of supplying drug addicts and as his GP you must decide what you are supposed to do.
  - Should smoking while pregnant be illegal?
  - What would you do if someone in your friendship group makes a racist comment?
  - What implications does BREXIT have on the NHS?
  - Why do you want to study medicine here?
  - Why does PBL suit you?
  - What experience do you have of independent learning?
  - What can go wrong with PBL?
  - What would you do if someone doesn't pull their weight in a team?
  - What do you prefer about PBL to the more traditional learning?
  - Lots of questions on team work / leadership

- Lots of questions on empathy and when you have shown it
- How do you deal with stress?
- Why do doctors get stressed?

Imperial Medical School
(BMAT)

Imperial have an MMi style interview which lasts about 45 minutes. They are looking for: Motivation and realistic approach to medicine as a career. Capacity to deal with stressful situations. Evidence of commitment to the values of NHS constitution. Evidence of working a s a leader and a team member. Ability to multi-task. Likely contribution to university life. Communication skills and maturity of character.

- What is blood pressure?
- What is the normal blood pressure?
- When would someone have high blood pressure?
- Why is blood pressure so important?
- What famous scientist do you most admire and why?
- How do you cope with stress?
- How do you know when you are getting stressed?
- What are the four ethical principles of medicine?
- Should the NHS offer gastric band surgery on the NHS?
- Should euthanasia become legal?
- What are the attributes of a good doctor?
- Who is Andrew Wakeley? What damage did he do?
- How would you tackle obesity?
- What are your experiences of teamwork and leadership?
- Do you think leadership is more important that teamwork?
- Do you think leadership is more important for consultants than junior doctors?
- Is hospital medicine or general practice more difficult?
- What is the structure of the NHS?
- Why is medicine challenging?
- How do politics influence the NHS?
- Should patients be able to request to see a doctor of the same ethnicity as themselves?
- How good are you at multi-tasking?
- If you were given 20 billion to spend on the NHS, what would you with it?

- You are doctor in a private clinic. You have two patients in the waiting room; one of them has a problem with sex addition, and the other has a problem with drug addiction. You can only treat one. Which one would you treat?
- What are your likely contributions to university life?
- Take us through what you will be doing here over the next 6 years.
- What interests you most about our curriculum here?
- Can you tell us about an interesting experience, and what you learned from it about yourself?
- Can you tell us about a recent significant advance in medicine or science?
- Tell us about a book you have read recently and what you enjoyed most about it.
- What do you admire most in your personal life and why?
- If you caught your best friend cheating in his third year medical exam, what would you do about it?
- Is it right for doctors to feel for their patients?
- When have you showed empathy to a patient?
- Tell us about a group activity you organized. What did you learn from it.
- Can you think of a team situation where your communication skills have been vital? Tell us about the situation and how you helped?
- Should 'alternative or complimentary medicine' be funded by the NHS?
- Some Trusts are refusing to perform some elective operations on obese patients. Do you think it's right?
- What would you prefer in a doctor: bad communication skills with good knowledge, or good communication skills with not so good knowledge, and why?
- What does the term inequalities in health mean to you?
- What are the biggest difficulties facing doctors today?
- What do you understand by the term Holistic Medicine?
- Give us an example when you saw holistic medicine.
- Do all doctors practice holistic medicine?
- Tell me about the function of the liver and how does alcohol affect the liver.
- Would you give an alcoholic a liver transplant?
- From what you saw in your work experience, what would you most like to change and why?
- Are you a leader or a follower?
- What first inspired you to become a doctor?
- What did you learn from your work experience?

- What was difficult about your work experience?
- What stood out for you in your work experience?
- What qualities does a good doctor have?
- Tell me of a recent article, which caught your eye.
- You're a partner in a GP surgery. A new person comes in to register for the first time; what questions do you ask and what tests do you carry out?
- What sports teams will you join if you come here?
- What is the most important clinical skill?
- What would you do if a patient asks to see you after surgery hours?
- Should doctors be altruistic?
- Picture yourself on a wet November Saturday in your first year at Imperial; how would you spend your time?
- What is the importance of general knowledge to doctors?
- What are the bad points about medicine?
- Is the status of doctors getting better or worse?
- Tell me about what happens once you've qualified. What have you done to inform yourself about this?
- What is your weakness?
- What makes you anxious?
- I see you're a House Captain. What does this involve and what fundraising skills have you developed?
- Do you think doctors should be able to prescribe contraception to a 15-year-old patients without the knowledge of their parents?
- Should a smoker be given a lung transplant on the NHS?
- If parents and a doctor disagree on the course of treatment for a child, who should decide?
- Should the age of consent for sexual intercourse be reduced?
- Should cosmetic surgery be allowed on the NHS?
- Is it ever justified for a doctor to breach confidentiality?
- Do you think NICE should license drugs more quickly?
- Have you ever failed at something? How did that make you feel?
- If somebody on your team made a mistake, what would you do?
- If you made a mistake with a patient, what would you do?
- Specific examples of leadership / teamwork
- What part does humour play in medicine?
- A lot of people do community work just to get into medical school. What have you done to show commitment?
- Why should we choose you?
- Why did you not choose a research career?

- How would you deal with an aggressive patient?
- What are your favourite subjects and topic areas?
- Name 3 things discovered / pioneered in the last 100 years that have prevented early death.
- What will you bring to Imperial as a person? What are the qualities of a good doctor?
- How do you deal with stress and approach exams?
- What clubs / societies are you be interested in joining?
- Which will be a bigger issue in 10 years time: cancer or Alzheimer's? Why?
- Questions regarding teamwork in general, and how have you exhibited such characteristics?
- Whether politicians or clinicians should run the NHS?
- Give me an example how you showed leadership.
- How do you deal with conflict?
- Tell us about the obesity epidemic and what would you do to increase public awareness and reduce the level of obesity.

Keele Medical School

In addition to the MMI, there is a numeracy skill (data handling) assessment. The numeracy / data handling assessment consists of 20 questions with a 30-minute time limit. The questions require you to perform simple calculations for a variety of different situations. Simple calculators are provided.

Keele assess you on the following attributes:
- Motivation / experiences informing your decision to pursue a medical career
- Empathy and insight
- Responsibilities and challenges of being a doctor
- Awareness of ethical issues in health and society
- Resilience
- Comprehension
- Effective communication

Each station at Keele is 5 minutes long, and there are eleven stations.
- You are shown a video demonstrating how to stabilise a broken leg. You then repeat the procedure on a lady with a broken leg who had just had a bicycle accident

- You are shown a bunch of cards, with each naming a quality in medicine. You have put them in order of importance.
- What have you done to prepare for medicine?
- You are asked about the spiral curriculum. What are 'inter-professional learning experiences' and why will these styles suit you as a student?
- Video: A girl with eating disorder blames mannequins for promoting unhealthy body dysmorphia /eating disorders in females. You are asked to comment on this.
- Video: A GP is talking to a patient who wants an abortion. However, he is constantly asking her, in a shocked tone, what her husband John will say about an abortion. You have to comment on this.
- Ethics: A teenage pregnant woman in pain comes into hospital demanding morphine. She has already been to demands more morphine. Has says she has already been to several other hospitals and that their tests have not shown any irregularities.
- You're a doctor who is just going off duty. You have opera tickets and you are meeting your wife at the opera. However, one of your patients has fallen ill and requires attention. Do you: a) stay and miss the opera, b) inform the next doctor on the shift what is going on c) go to the opera
- You're a doctor who has built a good relationship with an old lady who is your patient. She passes away. Do you a) send condolences to her family, b) attend the funeral, c) seek help from friends, d) seek help from a professional body
- Role play: You are told that you have to take a patient with Dementia for a walk, and make sure he puts his jumper on before you leave. You get him up and walk him towards the door but he keeps going back and sitting back down and repeatedly asks you if you want tea. At the end, they ask you how you think you coped, and how do you think you could improve.
- Other questions include: Why Keele? Why Medicine?
- Tell me a bit about your PBL course here.
- Why do you think the PBL course structure suits you?
- What can go wrong with PBL?
- What are the advantages and disadvantages of small group learning? Lots of questions on team player/ team leader
- There is a station on your roles and responsibilities. What skills and qualities have you shown during your work experience and what you have learnt? You have to expand on each point.

University of Kent and Canterbury Christ Church Medical School

When selecting our students, we will be looking for:
- A resilient all-rounder who can demonstrate a number of skills and attributes
- A realistic and committed attitude to medical training and clinical practice
- A commitment to quality of care, compassion and improving lives
- An understanding of NHS core values and the ability to reflect on their importance
- The ability to communicate and work effectively in a team, for the benefit of patients
- An appreciation of the need to treat people with dignity and respect
- The ability to appreciate other people's points of view
- A willingness to accept responsibility

KMMS is working in partnership with Brighton and Sussex Medical School. Please see Brighton and Sussex for their MMI Stations.

King's Medical School

King's College London MMI has between seven and eight stations, with 1-2 tasks per station. Candidates are allowed between five and seven minutes per station depending on the tasks being completed. Candidates are assessed on the following areas:
- Kindness, compassion and empathy, respect for the individual, privacy and dignity, advocacy, decision-making, team working and integrity.

They also state that 'some scenarios are scientifically based and designed to assess information-handling and evaluation-skills, whilst others will assess knowledge on topical medical issues'.

King's College place a great deal of emphasis on ethical issues. At the beginning of the interview, you are given a A4 sheet on which they give an outline of an ethical scenario. You are expected to discuss this at one of the stations. Keep in mind the four ethical principles of medicine.

Station 1: You are given a picture of a painting and asked to describe it. One picture used is a busy street scene with trams.

When I had finished describing the scene, they asked me why they asked me to describe a picture.

(You must describe the scene in minute detail until they tell you to stop). They are testing your power of observation and attention to detail, both of which are needed by doctors.

Station 2: What have you done to show commitment to medicine?

Station 3: Define resilience. When do you think personal resilience has to be shown in medical school? When have you shown resilience in your current everyday life?

Station 4: You are a GP. A 40-year-old patient is suffering from back pains, and this is his first time experiencing such pain. You recommend physiotherapy and painkillers. However, he is asking for a referral. What do you do?

Station 5: You are given a Graph regarding 3 chemotherapy treatments: drug A, drug B, and drug A+B. They asked questions on the risks and benefits, and asked to calculate the stage where 25% of cells are killed. You must also describe the efficiency of each treatment, also describe the graph as a whole, and answer more general questions on drug prescriptions.

Station 6: Your GP colleague tells you he has been out late drinking, and asks you to cover for him whilst he rests for an hour, and that he will then see the remaining patients. What would you do?

Station 7: Your classmate has recently suffered racial abuse online, and now appears to be withdrawn at school. What would you do?

- What would you do if a friend self-harms?
- They asked about work experience and emotional experience. (loads on emotional experience questions). They wanted an example, which really grabbed you?
- Do you like working in groups? Are you a leader?
- When have you worked in a team? What did you learn from this? What is a multidisciplinary team? When did you see an MDT in medicine? There are lots of questions on teamwork and leadership.
- Your friend has been the victim of bullying online. What would you do?
- You're in charge of a team, and a team member is not pulling his weight. What would you do?
- Describe a time when you've had to improve. What was it and what did you do?
- What do you understand by the term resilience? Why is it important in medicine?
- How have you shown resilience?

- What is empathy? When have you shown it? How important is it in medicine? Can someone learn empathy?
- There is a station on diabetes: What is it? You are shown a graph and asked to describe it. What are the causes of diabetes, and why is it so prevalent among certain groups?

Lancaster Medical School
BMAT

The MMI will consist of 12 to 14 'stations', which will be about 5 minutes long. Some stations will consist of a mini interview, where you may be asked questions about your career choice, work experiences or suitability for a medical career.

Other stations may be more interactive. You may be asked to read a short paragraph, or watch a video clip and then discuss the information at the following station.

There will be an additional 20-minute station, which will involve group work and will assess your suitability for problem-based learning.

Discuss an ethical scenario. You will have 5 minutes to: read a short paragraph that outlines an ethical dilemma, make notes, and consider your opinion. You will then have a further 5 minutes to discuss your thoughts with an examiner.

You read a PBL scenario and identify the most important points then justify why you thought they are important. You have 10 minutes to read and analyse the case, and a further 5 minutes at the next station to discuss your choices.

They explore your understanding of your chosen career, through discussion of your work and voluntary experience, including what you learned about your own suitability to be a doctor from these experiences.

You talk to a "family friend" or "neighbour" played by an actor. This will involve asking questions and responding to what the actor tells you. You must demonstrate compassion, empathy, respect etc.

More Questions:

- By referring to your personal statement, explain why do you intend to be a doctor?
- You are asked ethical questions e.g. on Down's syndrome and prenatal karyotyping.
- You watch a video, and then answer questions, which test your power of observation, and your attention to detail. e.g. What colour is the car in the video, or how many sheep were standing up, and how many sitting down?
- Why is teamwork important?
- What are the challenges of medicine?
- What did you learn from your work experience?
- What are the qualities of a good doctor?
- Which qualities do you not have?
- What surprised you about your medical work experience?
- When did you see good leadership in your work experience?
- How important is leadership in medicine?
- What are the different types of communication in medicine?
- When did you see good communication during your work experience?
- What are the qualities of a good team player?
- What are the qualities of a good team leader?
- Why is team working so important in medicine?
- Are you a leader or a follower?

Role Play Stations:

- When reverse your car, you run over, and kill, your neighbour's cat. She is elderly and lives alone. The cat is her companion. You have to visit her and break the bad news. She is very angry and upset.
- You bump into your neighbour's car when you are reversing. He bought the car yesterday. Talk to him.
- You are looking after your neighbour's canary whilst she is on holidays. You open the cage to clean it out, but the canary escapes and flies away. Talk to your neighbour when she returns.
- You call in to chat with your elderly neighbour whose husband died 3 weeks previously.
- Your friend has been passed over again for promotion. She is very upset. You call in to see her.
- An elderly patient arrives on good time for his appointment. He doesn't like to be late. However, there is an emergency and the doctor is delayed. The elderly man is kept waiting for an hour. Nobody bothers to

explain the situation. Eventually you have to talk to him. He is very upset.

- Another elderly patient arrives for his hospital appointment. When he checks in at reception, he is told that his appointment has been cancelled, but wasn't informed. He has come a long distance, changing buses several times. He is upset. You have to talk to him.
- After the role-play, they ask you how you think you performed; what you did well and not so well, and how you could improve.
- One station has a video of a doctor's consultation with a patient. You have to comment on what the doctor did well and not so well.

Some Questions:
- How do you react to stress?
- A question on obesity.
- What would you do if your medical colleague gave a patient the wrong prescription?
- When would you break confidentiality?
- Why is pre-natal screening important? Should it be optional?

Data interpretation station:
- You are shown graphs, or charts, or tables of data and asked questions about the data.
- There is a video about a doctor and patient consultation. You have to say what he did well and not so well.
- For example: The doctor had open body language, good eye contact, and spoke clearly. However, he answered his mobile phone, and did not apologise. The patient now has a sore toe; on previous visits she has a sore back. During this visit, the doctor kept talking about her back pain and not her toe pain. The patient became very frustrated.
- You had to talk about the strengths and weaknesses of the doctor.
- He slouched in his chair, and obviously wasn't paying attention.

Other Questions:
- Why Lancaster?
- What is positive and negative about our course?
- What did you learn from your work experience?
- How did you develop your skills during your work experience?
- Why did you do work experience?
- What experience did you do?
- What did you learn from it?

- What are the challenges of a doctor?

You have to fill in a form rating a doctor's performance (shown on the video) with a score ranging from 1 to 5.

The doctor should introduce himself, speak slowly and clearly, listen carefully, show empathy, confirm that the patient understands the diagnoses and ask if they have questions, and put the patient at ease. He should not answer his mobile phone, or display a lack of attention, or rush the patient.

Leeds Medical School
(BMAT)

The University of Leeds uses an eight-station multiple mini interviews to inform their selection. Each station lasts seven minutes. There is one minute of transition between stations / to read instructions for the following station.

Skills that are being assessed are:
- Ethical reasoning
- Self-evaluation
- Communication skills
- Problem-solving

They ask you detailed questions on your BMAT section three essay, so once you have completed your BMAT examination (months before your interview), note down the key points you made and look at how you could improve on your essay.

You have to read and comment on a given a newspaper article about Statins: The article itself can be found at the following link: http://www.express.co.uk/life-style/health/633160/Cholesterol-drug-statins-cause-heart-disease-experts.

The stations were as follows:

1. **BMAT essay**: Why did you choose this essay, and not one of the others? How would you improve your essay? What would you have said, if you had chosen a different essay?

2. **Ethics of euthanasia:** Discuss the pros and cons. What is the Dying Act Bill?

3. **Role play:** You are vising your elderly neighbour whose wife died three weeks previously.

4. **Situational judgement:** You are a medical student. On your day off from a GP placement, you bump into a patient from the practice. In confidence, the patient tells you about a medical condition he has, but insists that you do not tell the GP. The interviewer gives you 5 responses, and you have to place them in order of suitability.

5. **Work experience;** You are asked to discuss the challenges of being a doctor, with examples from your work experience. Then, you have to discuss how the challenges may put off some students from studying medicine, and explain why.

6. **Discussed article:** Read and discuss a newspaper article on Statins. You have to discuss not only the content of the article, but also comment on whether or not such articles should be published in public newspapers. Is it ethical for papers to publish this, should clinical studies be accessible to the public, and how might the article impact the readers.

7. **Teamwork:** Discuss teamwork. When and where did you work in a good team, and in a bad team? What made the difference between the good team and the bad team? What would you have done differently?

8. **Advice:** Write down the three most important bits of advice you would give yourself, as you enter medical school. Then discuss each one in detail.

Leicester Medical School

The University of Leicester uses the multiple mini interview format to make its selection. There are eight stations which assess the following:
- Motivation to study medicine and genuine interest in the medical profession
- Personal attributes, for example: honesty, emotional intelligence, resilience, conscientiousness, personal organisation, ability to work as a team member
- Academic ability and problem-solving skills
- Ability to reflect on your work, strengths, weaknesses, as well as your own health
- Effective communication, including reading, writing, listening and speaking

- Ability to deal with uncertainty, manage risks, deal with problems and take responsibility for your actions
- Ability to be empathetic and treat people with compassion, respect and dignity
- Ethical Judgement

Station 1
- You are shown a video of a fifth year medical student taking a patient's medical history. Then, you have to fill in a form about the patient: for example with headings like this: Age, sex, marital status, previous illness, previous surgery, medication, etc.

Station 2
Role Play:
- The instruction says: you are doing work experience in an office. Talk to a man who is waiting for an interview or meeting.

Station 3
- You are shown a video about a patient collecting a repeat prescription from the GP's receptionist. You are asked questions about the interaction between the receptionist and patient.

Station 4
- Testing English: You are given three minutes to read an article. You then return the article, and the interviewer asks you questions about it. One article is based on anticancer drugs.

Station 5
Poster Station:
- You have to present your poster, which you have completed previously. The interviewer then asks you to discuss it, and answer specific questions about it.

Station 6
Role Play:
- Instruction says: You are at a GP surgery on work experience. You have to talk to the patients, as there is a slight delay to see the GP.

Station 7

Maths Station:

- You are given a graph: 'Paracetamol Overdose Curve'.
- You are asked to describe the graph, and asked detailed questions about it. For example: how would you use this graph to treat a patient who has taken too much paracetamol? They give you some 'readings' for a patient, and ask you whether or not you would prescribe Acetylcysteine.

Station 8

Question Station – general questions

- What is the difference between a doctor and a nurse?
- If you were running the course, how would you encourage more students to become GPs?
- What 4 qualities are important for a doctor?
- Who would be blamed if something went wrong in hospital: the nurse or the doctor?

Lincoln Medical School

See Nottingham Medical School for the MMI questions.
Interviews are held at both Nottingham and Lincoln. The style of interviews will be Multiple Mini-Interview (MMI), and will comprise 8 stations. They are the same at both sites.

- In the first station you enter, you will be asked 'ice-breaker' questions, for two minutes. All applicants are asked the same questions and the answers are not scored
- After two minutes, the assessment for that station starts and the station lasts for five minutes
- There is one minute to exit the station and read the instructions outside the next station
- Then a five-minute assessment in the next station

The eight station formats are:

- Two stations will involve role play
- Six stations will involve answering questions based on the instructions or scenarios that are provided outside the station. A copy of the instructions or scenarios is also in the station for you to refer to during the assessment

The interview is designed to assess the personal qualities we consider essential for the practice of medicine. You will be expected to have good communication and listening skills, an understanding of professional issues such as teamwork, and respect for the contribution of those working in professions allied to medicine.

Liverpool Medical School

Liverpool University uses a seven-station multiple mini interview (MMI). Each station is six-minutes in duration, with a one-minute break between. The main attributes assessed are:
- Communication
- Team-working
- Ethics
- Learning from work experience/caring contribution
- Numeracy

Station 1: Personal Statement: You are given 10 qualities of a doctor and asked to choose 3. Then you have to discuss those qualities by making reference to your personal statement.

Station 2: Teamwork: You are given a scenario: A girl, who is a member of a group doing a project, sends texts to her group members but they do not reply. So, the girl works independently on the project. The interview then asks you to discuss the scenario, and asks two specific questions: should the professor be worried about this girl not being able to work in a group, and how could she improve?

Station 3 & 4: Ethical scenario: A patient underwent a planned surgery on his colon. During the surgery, his appendix was also removed. The patient was not informed that his appendix would be removed. After surgery, a doctor makes the following comment: 'You no longer have an appendix'. You are asked this question: What are the arguments for and against the patient having cause to complain?

Station 5: Work Experience: What did you learn from your work experience? What do you like most and least about medicine? How would you deal with the stress of being a doctor?

Station 6: Health Issues: You are asked to read an article about alcoholism in the UK. You are asked to discuss the article and to offer ways of reducing alcoholism. Another question: if you were given the budget of the NHS how would I set to improve it? And what would be your main priority if you had limited money to improve the NHS?

Station 7: Maths Station: You are given data on drug dosage, and asked to calculate the dosage for a specific patient. You are given the details of the patient.

Manchester Medical School

Candidates are interviewed in a seven-station multiple mini interview (MMI). Each station has an interviewer and will be seven minutes long, with a two-minute gap between stations. The interview assesses the following areas:
- details in your non-academic information form or personal statement
- motivation to study medicine as a career
- communication
- problem solving
- capacity for self-reflection
- capacity for logical thinking
- understanding of professional responsibility
- capacity for working in a team
- ability to discuss issues of a wider nature, in the field of medicine.

Station 1 Non Academic:
- What have you learnt from your work experience?
- What did you learn as a healthcare assistant?
- How do you de-stress?
- What did your army-cadet experience teach you?
- Discuss the impact of social media for doctors.
- What did you learn from shadowing the GP?

Station 2
Role Play Station: A medical colleague isn't washing his hands between patients. You have to talk to him. At the end, you have to reflect on how the consultation went.

Station 3

There is a discussion about GMC guidelines. They have a selection of quotes and they chose one of them, and you have to discuss what that quote means to you.

Station 4

You have to discuss the pros and cons of Euthanasia.

Station 5

Role Play:

You work for a charity which takes the elderly on outings. One elderly gentleman doesn't want to go on the outing. You talk to him. He says the minibus driver and another patient are rude to him, but he doesn't want to cause a fuss.

Station 6

You forgot to prescribe medication to a patient, and are now at a routine multidisciplinary team meeting. What would you do?
In another scenario, you see a visitor go into the ward office and look at confidential information. What would you do?

Station 7

There are various scenarios: discuss GMC guidelines, explain what you would do if you caught your friend cheating.

Newcastle Medical School

The medicine school interview consists of a seven-station Multiple Mini Interview (MMI). Each station lasts seven minutes with an extra two minute ice breaker question in the first station. One of the stations involves a role-play; others may be question-based or task-driven. Applicants are assessed on the following categories:

- Integrity (honesty and probity)
- Communication
- Empathy and self-awareness
- Motivation and commitment to be a doctor
- Compatibility with the MBBS programme
- Teamwork (including leadership)
- Personal organisation
- Persistence and resilience

STATION 1: Role-play
One of your medical school classmates is depressed. You talk to him. After a little probing, he said he is feeling a bit isolated and doesn't know many people on the course.
After the role-play, you are asked what went well, and not so well?

STATION 2: Newcastle and the course itself
You are asked to talk about Newcastle, and why you will like living there. You also talk about the course structure and why it suits you. You may also be asked about the 'base units'.

STATION 3: Commitment to medicine
You are asked about the challenges in medicine, the qualities of a doctor, and your work experience. After stating quite a few, you may be cut off. You may be asked about your career plans, the intercalated degree, how long it takes to become a consultant, and what research you are interested in.

STATION 4: Teamwork and leadership
Here they ask about the qualities of a good team, and if you have been in a bad team, and what happened with that. They ask for a time when you lead a team and how that went? There are lots of questions on teamwork and leadership. How important is teamwork and leadership in medicine? When did you see good teamwork in your work experience?

STATION 5: Organisational Skills
How good are your organisational skills? How do you deal with stress? How do you organise yourself when you have a lot to do?How do you know when you are stressed? Why do doctors get stressed?

STATION 6: How you respond to mistakes
The interviewer basically asked four variations of this question: what was a recent mistake you made, and what was a bad decision you made recently, and what did you learn from that?

STATION 7: Ethics
There were two main questions, and then follow up questions depending on what you said.
The first question was: "Tell me about a recent ethical case in the news".
The next question was: "Tell me about a morally difficult situation you were in".

Nottingham Medical School

Nottingham University Medicine interviews consist of eight Multiple Mini Interview (MMI) stations. There are two stations which involve role-play and six which are question and answer-based. At each station, candidates are given one minute to read the instructions outside the station, and then five minutes to complete the assessment tasks. At the first station, students are asked 'ice-breaker' questions for the first three minutes before beginning their first five minute assessment task. These are not part of the MMI assessment but are designed to prepare the candidate for the rest of the stations. The MMI lasts approximately one hour.

1. Ice breaker (not marked); When did you realise that you wanted to do medicine? The actual question: One of your colleagues in the medical school has a bruise on her face. You are then asked possible causes, and what would you actually do in this situation.

2. This station had the scenario: You are in a car crash and your mother and brother are injured. You are then given about 10 cards on which are additional events occurring at the same time as the car crash. For example: an elderly lady is unconscious on the floor. You have to prioritise the events in under a minute, and then explain your choices.

3. You are given a statement from the GMC saying: "Medical professionals should not discriminate against their patients or colleagues." Then you are asked to basically elaborate on this.

4. The next station was a role play: a fellow student doesn't want to attend choir and you have to persuade him to go.

5. Scenario: you are doing work experience in a GP practice and a patient tells you in confidence that he still smokes, even though he told the doctor he doesn't. You are asked why might the patient have done this, and what would you actually do.

6. You then had to test a urine sample, and explain the results. You are asked when might a urine test be required.

7. You have to help an elderly lady fill out a form for a free bus pass.

At the final station, you have to talk about anything during school or work experience that made you angry. One student said how socio-economic inequality in Pakistan meant some people weren't able to get good care, just because they were poor. He was then asked how this changed him, so he said it taught him the importance of being non-judgemental, and to appreciate the NHS.

A scenario: You are a team leader in a D of E group. One of the girls is an amazing cook and loves cooking, but she says she doesn't want to cook again. You have to speak to her.

Why Nottingham? Why medicine?

- A roleplay: You are a junior doctor. A patient has breast cancer. Your consultant wants you to talk to her about what happens next and also to console her.
- What do you think about the Staffordshire nursing failures? Why do you think it happened? What can we do to prevent it happening again?
- A man who has terminal neurodegenerative disease has suggested he wants to pass away now. Discuss this scenario and the issues surrounding it.
- Roleplay: Your FY1 colleague is taking drugs, and you have become aware of this situation. Sit down with him and talk to him . Try to persuade him to stop.
- What constraints does the NHS face?

Other questions:
- You are at a shopping centre with your mother and younger brother when there is an explosion in the centre. You are given 10 cards on which are written suggestions of what you could do. You are asked to put them in order of priority, and explain your choices of order.
- Discuss the following quote from the GMC: "Doctors should always act in the best interest of the patient".
- Build a model of a giraffe while discussing the pros and cons of euthanasia.
- Role play: You are a volunteer at a citizen's advice centre. An elderly man asks for assistance in filling out a form applying for financial assistant to pay his rent.
- Role play: You are taking your friend to a school play in which he has the lead role. When you come to collect him, he is on his phone. He ignores you, and stays on his phone. Find out what's wrong.

- Role Play: You are on work experience in a GP practice. The GP leaves the room mid-appointment, and the patient confides that he has stolen apples on his way to the appointment.
- Discuss a moment from your work experience, in the caring area , that surprised you, and what did you learnt from it?

OXBRIDGE
(Cambridge and Oxford Medical School)
BMAT

Oxbridge concentrates more on the basic sciences behind medicine. They want to make finer judgment about your academic ability and potential; something A level predictions cannot provide.

They want to see how well you can think on your feet; how clearly and logically you can express the results of your though processes. Often they will give you a problem to solve. Don't be afraid to admit you don't know the solution, but say you will try to work through a possible solution.

Above all, show your enthusiasm and energy for their medical school. In Oxbridge they still offer the traditional medical degree where the first three years are academic, and the final years are clinical.

- How would you solve the AIDS crises in Africa?
- How does the body recognise and remove poison in the body?
- Why do you not see many stars when you stand on top of a mountain?
- Describe this timber log.
- How would you cope if you were not getting top grades, when you are studying here?
- If you had to look back to this year in ten years time, what would you tell people about it?
- For which disease do you think it is an advantage to be a carrier of cystic fibrosis?
- Who do you most admire and why?
- If your friends were here now instead of you, what would they say about you?
- At what point is a person dead?
- How can the reindeer tell the difference between spring and autumn?
- Should women have the right to choose whether to have caesarean or not, and why?

- How is a city like a cell?
- How many genes are there in a genome of a rice plant?
- How would you design a better brain?
- If urine was emptied from the intestine instead of the bladder, what would happen?
- Is denying an elderly patient invasive heart surgery age discrimination?
- You can invite any two people, alive or dead, to a dinner party. Who would you invite and why?
- What does the letter B stand for in a B-lymmphocyte?
- Why don't we have just one ear, in the middle of our face?
- This is a graph of life expectancy over the last 200 years. Explain why you think it looks the way it does.
- Should smokers be allowed a lung transplant?
- If you were a rat, what would be the most important thing to you?
- If your patient died because you made a mistake, what would you do?
- Is it an advantage for a virus to kill its host?
- Tell us about 3 medically related articles you have recently read in newspapers
- Draw graphs of blood levels of a drug against time: one if the drug is ingested orally, and the other if injected.
- If there is a baby in a supermarket with a bomb strapped to it, would you shoot the baby to save 100 people?
- What are the ethical issues raised by an elderly person in a coma with little hope of surviving?
- Why should we choose you over other candidates?
- What leaves you drier if it's raining: running or walking?
- You may be given a graph axis and asked to draw three graphs of plasma drug concentration against time for:
- The drug had been taken orally.
  - It is taken by IV
  - It is taken by IV at half the rate of the original IV
- Explain the graph at each point and describe what is happening. How is a drug removed from the kidneys and the liver?
- How does venous return work, and how does breathing help this?
- What evidence is there that mitochondria evolved from virus?
- How do you cope with conflict?
- What would you like people to remember about you from your medical school life?
- Do foetal lungs receive blood? If so, how?
- What is negative and positive feedback? Give examples in the body.

- What is blood pressure? Why is it important?
- How many DNA bases encode an amino acid? Why not 2 or 4?
- Why is diabetes bad?
- How are electrical signals generated and conducted in a neuron?
- What is Ohm's law? How can you apply it to the cardiovascular system?
- Talk to me about a patient you met during your work experience
- This is the last injection against a serious illness. Who should have it, you or me?
- Why is obesity rising in the UK, and what effect has it on the NHS?
- What is competency? How do you know a patient is competent?When would a patient be able to give consent?
- What are the disadvantages of a medical career?
- How do doctors keep themselves up-to-date?
- What would you do if one of the doctors in your team is lying?
- Tell me about an article you read recently
- How do you keep motivated?
- Which diseases are caused by single gene disorders?
- Is there more to medicine that applied science?
- Which scientist over the past century do you most admire?
- Tell me the role of the stomach in digestion
- How do you cope with stress?
- If you had to lose one part of your brain, what would you chose and why?
- How do enzymes in the pancreas digest food in the gut without digesting the pancreas itself? What would happen to the body if these mechanisms failed?
- How would you weigh your head, without chopping it off?
- Tell me about DNA and how it makes protein
- What is Haemoglobin? How does its structure affect its biological properties i.e. carrying oxygen?
- What makes you apply to this particular college?
- Describe the characteristics of living organisms
- Describe the role of microorganisms and fermenters in production of penicillin
- Describe the problems of world food supplies and the problems that contribute to famine
- What are the social implications of the increase in the world population?
- Why does your heart rate increase with exercise?
- Tell me about a banana.

- What was the last book you read and what interested you most about the book?
- What do you like about our course?
- What are the Neo-Darwin theories of evolution?
- How can bacteria be genetically engineered to produce human insulin?
- How does HIV affect the immune system?
- How could you simulate altitude in your living room?
- On a hot day, what should you do with a fridge?
- Tell me four ways in which coordination by the nervous system differs from coordination by hormones
- If a carrot can grow from carrot cell, why not a human?
- Describe the process of blood clotting
- What are the risk factors in the development of heart disease?
- Tell me the events of the cardiac cycle
- Tell me about drowning
- What do you think of assisted suicide?
- Would you give a 60-year-old woman IVF treatment? What are the reasons for considering IVF as ethically wrong?
- What is the point of using NHS money to keep old people alive?
- How would you poison someone without the police finding out?
- If you were a grapefruit, would you rather be seedless or have seeds?
- Why is it a disadvantage for humans to have two legs?
- What do you like most about the brain?
- How would you describe a human to a Martian?
- How many footballs can you fit into an airplane?
- How would you design an experiment to find out which part of the brain controls emotions?
- How much water is there in a horse?
- How many animals did Noah take on the Ark?
- Tell me the health hazards associated with food additives
- How does the liver break down alcohol?
- Is hell exothermic or endothermic?
- Describe the roles of the immune system in antibody production.
- Tell me the internal structure of the kidney
- How high can I climb a mountain, having eaten only one banana?
- How can paper be recycled?
- Are humans still evolving?
- In Africa, how can sewage treatment make water safe?
- What food is best to eat before an interview?
- Is medicine a science or an art, and why?

Plymouth Medical School

The interviews follow a Multiple Mini Interview (MMI) structure. You will be assessed across seven single-assessor stations. The interview will take approximately 50 minutes.

We place great value on the following qualities, and we are looking for you to demonstrate these at your interview:
- integrity
- veracity and honesty
- flexibility
- motivation and commitment
- empathy and being non-judgmental
- communication skills
- potential for leadership
- insight into the roles and responsibilities of a doctor, dentist, dental care professional or healthcare scientist
- ability to be a team player
- ability to deal with stress appropriately
- problem solving skills
- students who know their limitations, their strengths and weaknesses
- reflectiveness
- students who demonstrate a suitable approach to life and people

Station 1
- The interviewer gives you 20 minutes to guess what organ of the body he is thinking about. He responds with 'yes' or 'no.'

Station 2
- A patient on your ward has a history of violent outbursts. The ward is understaffed. How would you protect the other patients? What security measures would you put in place?
- What aspect of the working life of a doctor appeals to you?
- Why have you chosen medicine?
- What are your qualities?
- What have you done to improve your suitability for medicine?

Station 3

- What is empathy? When have you displayed empathy? How important is empathy in medicine? Can empathy be taught at medical school?
- How does a disabled child impact the whole family?

Station 4

Communication:

- You have an A4 sheet of paper on which are displayed various geometrical shapes in various colours. You have to instruct a man to reproduce the shapes and colours on his blank sheet of paper using coloured crayons. The man has learning difficult, and a low attention span.

Station 5

- A patient is addicted to alcohol and has liver failure. How would it affect him and his whole family?

Station 6

- When have you worked in a team? How have you improved by working in a team?
- What makes a good team? When were you in a bad team?
- When did you have to make an important decision?
- What is your greatest mistake? What did you learn from that? What would you do differently?
- How important is teamwork in medicine?

Station 7

- What did you learn from your work experience?
- What are the qualities of a doctor?
- What are the challenges of medicine?
- What are the advantages and disadvantages of PBL? When have you done PBL?
- Give me clear verbal instructions on how to tie my shoe laces. Do not use your hands.
- Why medicine? Why Plymouth?
- A patient collapses in the GP waiting room. What would you do and say?
- How do you cope with stress and why is copying with stress important for a doctor?
- What did you learn from your work experience?

- What would you do if you failed to get into medicine this year?
- What would you do differently when giving instructions to: a group of young children, a group of teenagers, a group of elderly people, and a mixed group of the three categories?
- How does disease affect a person?

Queen Mary's (Bart's) Medical School A100

Queen Mary's have a traditional interview lasting around 20 minutes. The panel consist of two senior academics or clinical staff, a medical student and sometimes a lay person. The interview is not intended to be an intimidating experience, and staff will try to put you at ease while evaluating:

- your motivation and realistic approach to medicine as a career
- whether you show initiative, resilience and maturity
- whether you work well as part of a team
- your organisational and problem-solving abilities, and your ability to communicate effectively.

Typical Questions:
- Discuss the article we sent you.
- Why medicine?
- Why Bart's?
- What will be different about being at Bart's, compared to other medical schools?
- What is teamwork? What makes a good team? What makes a good leader?
- Tell us about an article you recently read in the student BMJ
- What could be one disadvantage of a PBL course?
- Is there anything about you that you would like to mention?
- Why Medicine?
- Why Bart's?
- What is teamwork all about?
- What are the negative aspects of working as a doctor?
- How do doctors cope with one of their patients dying?
- What challenges would you face coming to Bart's, rather than to another medical school?
- Why study here in the East End of London?
- Why do you want to do medicine, considering the current state of the NHS?

- Why do you think you will make a good doctor?
- Tell us about a specific patient who interests you
- How do doctors deal with uncertainty?
- How would a doctor break bad news to a patient?
- Give us an example when you showed leadership.
- Did you have any stressful situations during your work experience?
- In what groups are you involved?
- What makes the difference between a good team and a bad team?
- What specific problems can doctors face in the surrounding poor and multi ethnic areas of London?
- What makes an effective team?
- What did you notice when you came out of the tube station?

Queen's University Medical School Belfast

Queen's University Belfast (QUB) uses multiple-mini interviews (MMI) to test for the desired competencies for entry into their MBBS programme. The interview has nine stations in total, with three of these as 'rest' stations. You are given one minute to prepare for the station and five minutes at the station itself to complete the task/answer questions. The stations focus on the following non-cognitive competencies:
- Empathy
- Problem solving
- Moral reasoning
- Communication skills

Station 1: Describe how you would go about assessing a presentation given by one of your peers.

Station 2: (Role play). You are the safety officer of an Aer Lingus flight. Your task is to assist a blind individual with signing a sheet stating that they have no dangerous items on their person.

Station 3: Would you initiate a scheme where students who have received the meningitis vaccine, get significantly lower tuition fees. What are the pros and cons; what alternatives could be used?

Station 4: Are patients allowed to know doctors' wages?

Station 5: (Role play) You see your friend selling alcohol to under-aged children in a night club, and the children go on to be physically sick and inebriated.

Station 6: (Role play) You see your friend selling cigarettes to kids at the bus stop.

Station 7: (Role play) Your patient's sister (who is also your patient) comes in worried about the way her sister is behaving (alcoholism, kids missing school) and wants to know what is going on with her.

Station 8: Discuss the skills and qualities leaned from work experience

Station 9: You are presented with two pieces of legislation:

1. Over 65s get double the voting weight, 21+ get normal weight, under 21 get half weighted votes.
2. Over 65s get half the voting weight, 21+ get normal weight, under 21 get double weighted votes.
   What are the pros and cons of each?
   Which would you choose?

Sheffield Medical School

The Multiple Mini-Interviews comprise a series of eight 8 stations which last 8 minutes.

The questioning is typically based around the following areas:
- Communication skills
- Depth and breadth of interests (achievements in specific fields)
- Evidence of commitment for caring
- Knowledge of and interest in studying in Sheffield
- Medical work experience/Extended Project Qualification
- Motivation for medicine
- Understanding the nature of medicine
- Values and attitudes
- Outside interests

Station 1
- If you are successful in your application you may be spending 5 years living and studying in Sheffield. What can you tell me about the City of Sheffield and the University of Sheffield?
- What do you know about the Sheffield MBChB curriculum?

Station 2
Objectives:
- Medicine in a wider context
- To explore why the candidate wants to be a doctor, what they learnt from their work experience (including what they know about the working of the NHS), and what the candidate knows about current controversies that surround medical practice.

Questions:
- What inspired you to want to become a doctor?
- Tell me about a patient who you saw, during your work experience or volunteering, who inspired you to find out more about what was wrong with them.
- Do you think that non-emergency services should be provided seven days a week, in the NHS?

Station 3
Good Medical Practice
Objectives: To explore the candidate's understanding of the importance of professional standards and values in Medicine.

Questions:
- What can you tell me about the General Medical Council's code of conduct for doctors?
- Do you think it might ever be appropriate to breach a patient's confidentiality? Can you give any examples?
- While working at your Saturday job in a shop, you find that one of your colleagues has arrived at work smelling of alcohol. They appear to be intoxicated, and you know that they drove to work. What actions would you take?

Station 4
Attitudes and values (Values Based Recruitment)

Objectives: To explore the attitudes, values and communication skills of candidates when placed into a situation with little time to prepare. These questions map to the values of the NHS Constitution.

Questions:
- Tell me about a time when you have made a positive impact on someone's life.
- Based on your work or voluntary experiences, what do you think are the challenges of delivering quality care to patients?
- How do you think demonstrating respect and dignity impacts on patients?

Station 5
Candidate as a person

Objectives: To explore the candidate's interests and hobbies, and his coping strategies.

Questions:
- Studying medicine can be intense, so maintaining a work-life balance is important. How do you relax and unwind?
- Medical students are selected from the best and the brightest students around the world. How will you cope with moving from an environment where you were one of the best students to one where everyone has a similar level of ability?
- As a doctor, you will have to break bad news and deal with things when they go wrong. How do you think you will cope with this emotionally?

Station 6
Communication skills

Objectives: To explore the candidate's communication skills and ability to interact with a patient.

Instructions to Candidate:
At this station, you will meet a patient with a long-term illness. You are asked to engage him in conversation and find out about the nature of his illness, how it is managed, what effect it has on his daily life, and how he thinks it is likely to affect his life in the future. The patient will be scoring you on your ability to interact with him.

Station 7: Ethics, values and attitudes
Objectives: To explore the ethics of the candidate and his understanding of the importance of professionalism and professional boundaries.

Questions:
- The use of social media websites such as Facebook is now widespread amongst the public, students and healthcare professionals. Is it appropriate for medical students and doctors to use such websites?
- How would you advise a doctor who is wondering whether or not to accept one of his patients, as a friend on a social media website such a Facebook?
- Should medical students and doctors always declare their profession/professional status when interacting with others on a social media website? Why?

Station 8
Information processing/Logic

Objectives: To explore the applicant's ability to process and store knowledge
Instructions to candidate:
- At this station, you will be asked to play a round of "20 Questions" to identify an object, creature, event or place that is known to the interviewer. To determine the answer, you must ask the interviewer a series of questions. The interviewer has been instructed to answer only 'YES' or 'NO' to your questions. You may ask up to 20 questions. All questions must be answerable by 'YES' or 'NO'. You are being scored on the logical approach of the questioning, and not on whether you identify the correct answer.

Southampton Medical School

The interview is in two parts. The first part is a 20 minutes informal panel interview, with two interviewers.

The second part of the interview is a group task lasting approximately 30 minutes. The groups are made up of about 8 candidates who are assessed at the same time. The group is presented with an ethical issue which is summarised on a piece of paper with instructions. Two assessors are in the room. They are testing the following:

- Are self motivated and have initiative
- Are literate and articulate
- Are able to interact successfully with others
- Have learnt from your experiences of interacting with people in health or social care settings
- Understanding & respect of the NHS values
- Compassion, team working and treating others with respect and dignity

The panel interview is split into two sections: talking to one person for 10 minutes about oneself, and then to a different person for 10 minutes about a lot more knowledge-based questions. There are questions based on the personal statement:

- Why Southampton?
- How do you juggle all the activities you do?
- Have you ever failed at something? How did you cope?
- Where and at what have you volunteered?
- What has that taught you?
- Have you faced any difficulties when volunteering?
- Is there anything about the extracurricular activities at Southampton that you like?
- What do you think about some people having to pay for prescriptions/glasses, in some areas of the UK?
- Do you think the NHS should be rationed?
- Do you know how long it takes to become a consultant? How it is different to become a GP?
- Is the NHS compassionate towards its employees?
- Should the NHS train a specific percentage of students as GPs, as surgeons, etc?
- Do you think it is unethical to bring people who have trained overseas to work for the NHS?

The Panel Interview was almost entirely based on my personal statement, with the rest being standard questions.

- They asked about what I do as senior prefect and how that developed my leadership?
- Why medicine? Why Southampton?
- What is compassion?

There were a lot of questions on my volunteering and work experience, and follow up questions from that.

There were a few questions based on my half-marathon and what the wall was (which I thankfully knew)

- When have you made a large mistake?
- What did you learn/how were you affected by this experience (referring to an experience described in the personal statement)?
- How did you arrange this work experience?
- Questions on what extra-curricular activitie you hope to continue carrying on during university.
- Can you talk to us about a medically related book or article that you read recently? Then further questions on that book/topic.
- What did you learn about yourself by volunteering? How much time do you spend volunteering on that placement?
- Why would you like to study at Southampton?
- What do you think makes a good doctor? Why would you make a good doctor?
- Why do you want to study here?
- What appeals to you about this city?
- Why medicine, why not nursing or some other health professional course?
- Are there any areas in which you want to specialise?
- How will you handle the stresses of work?
- How will you balance work and extracurricular activities?
- What are your strengths and weaknesses?
- What difficulties do you think you will face and how will you tackle these?
- What's the biggest mistake you have ever made?
- Tell us about a team activity you organised. What went badly? What did you learn from that?
- Let's think ahead to when you are a doctor. Who do you think will be the most important person in your team? Are you a leader or a follower? Do teams need leaders?
- Can you tell me about a significant recent advance in Medicine?
- Do you think health care should be free or should people pay?
- Should the NHS be involved in non-essential surgery?
- Other than a lack of funds, what are the current issues within the NHS? Where do you see the NHS in 10 years time?

Examples of group discussion at Southampton

- Should a person who gives another person a sexually transmitted infection be given a prison sentence?
- Should smokers and obese patients be taken off the NHS waiting lists because other patients who do not smoke, and have a normal weight, are deemed to be more suitable candidates?
- Discuss the Four Ethical Principles of medicine.
- Why do we have an obesity epidemic in the UK and what can we be done about it?
- One of your friends is a third year medical students. He goes out drinking every Thursday night until 4 am. Every Friday in clinic he is not following infection control procedures. Discuss.
- A daughter who took her father to die in a clinic in Switzerland has been given to a two-year suspended jail sentence. Discuss
- What is your opinion on euthanasia? Group discussion.
- Should someone who has smoked for the last 20 years be entitled to free health care? Group discussion.
- The global population now exceeds 7 billion and could be described by many as overpopulated. Should the NHS fund IVF?
- Some drugs are legal whilst others are illegal. Discuss the issues surrounding drugs.

St Andrew's Medical School

St Andrew's use the multiple mini interview (MMI) format. It has six stations, each lasting six minutes with at least one station involving role-play and one is on an article they give you to read in advance. At the interview, you will be expected to demonstrate that you:
- Have an understanding of and commitment to medicine as a career
- Have shown a commitment to academic study, perseverance and intellection potential
- Appreciate the realities of working in a caring profession.
- Have excellent communication and interpersonal skills (e.g. empathy, leadership and team-working)
- An ability to discuss ethical issues.

Station 1. Role Play

- Explain a bus timetable to an elderly lady.
- Explain how to use an inhaler to an elderly woman.
- Help an elderly man in a community centre to sort out his coin collection.
- Demonstrate to a lady, who had just had her baby, how to change a nappy, and discuss the development stages in a baby.

Station 2

- Alan has accessed Jane's laptop without her permission and has taken parts of her essay and put it into his essay. He said it was because he didn't have time to complete the assignment by the deadline. What should Jane do (if anything) in this situation?

Station 3

- NHS funding is available. You have to decide where to allocate the funds.
- This is really a discussion about the problems facing the NHS, and about good patient care. For example: the obesity epidemic, the increase in the elderly population, drug and alcohol abuse, shortage of staff, bed blocking etc.

Station 4

- Why did you do work experience?
- What examples of good medical practice did you see on your work experience?
- Looking forward to your career in medicine, what are you looking forward to the most and the least?
- Why St Andrews? Explain the course and how it differs from normal courses?
- What qualification do you receive at the end? What can you go on to do after that?
- Questions about your personal statement.
- Why do you want to be a doctor and not a nurse?

Station 5

- You have 10 minutes to read an article and then they ask questions about it. (It's a good idea to jot down a quick summary as in the interview there was a question asking you to summarise the article, and how could it be improved).

Station 6

- You are given a very difficult (impossible) puzzle about making shapes. Then they ask:
- How do you feel that you couldn't do the puzzle?
- Why do you think you couldn't do it?
- Do you get upset when you can't solve a problem?

Other questions students were asked:

- Why St Andrews?
- What do you know about the course here?
- What will you be doing here?
- Why does this medical school appeal to you?
- What are the advantages of our course?
- What are its limitations?
- What have you gained from your work experience?
- How has your work experience prepared you for medicine?
- What methods of learning work best for you, and how does this fit in with here?
- How has the internet promoted bad healthcare?
- Is there a moral difference between turning off a life support machine for a coma patient, and a patient asking you to prescribe a drug to kill them?
- Do you least prefer public speaking or interviews, and what could you do to try and improve this?
- How does a patient with dementia affect the rest of the family?
- What types of people do you find it difficult to work with?
- What are the things that people do today and won't do in 100 years from now?
- What is the structure of the Scottish NHS?
- In what region of Scotland is St Andrew's?
- Should vaccinations be compulsory?
- What are the qualities of a good doctor?
- How do you know medicine is for you?
- What part of your work experience confirmed your desire to do medicine?
- What can you offer us?
- There are lots of questions on the personal statement.
- Who is the most important person in a team?
- How would you like a patient to describe you?
- What are your weaknesses?

- What is the biggest problem with the NHS?
- What would you like to do after you are qualified?
- What are some of the challenges about being a doctor and how would you deal with them?
- How good are your communication skills?
- How does a patient with dementia affect the rest of the family?
- Lots of questions on team player and leadership.

St George's Medical School

St. George's medicine interview is a multiple mini interview (MMI) that consists of eight stations each lasting for five minutes. The stations are extremely varied, including answering questions, solving problems, a video, prioritisation, and engaging in role-play.

They primarily aim to look at how good of a fit you are for medicine at the school. In doing so, they will assess your skills and qualities, including empathy, communication, organisation, and teamwork.

You are about to take up a place at medical school. A company owner then offers you a job as trainee manager with a company car and a starting salary of £40K. Your parents will have to make big financial sacrifices to see you through medical school. Discuss this.

Video station.
- A medical student colleague asks you to sign in for her at a lecture. She is very stressed out, and is very persuasive. She says it's not a big issue as people do it all the time, and she can catch up on the lecture notes, etc.
- What are the issues here, and what would you do?
- You work for British Airways (BA). An international flight has been cancelled and the previous evening you have notified the affected passengers. However, on the day of the planed flight, an elderly couple present themselves to check in. They have travelled today by coach from Aberdeen to Heathrow. You realise you did not notify this couple. Talk to them.

Other questions:
- What qualities do you have and how can you use these in Medicine?

- Tell me about a recent advancement in medicine history, and why is research important?
- What are the challenges in medicine?
- You have made a mistake with a diagnosis, the patient dies and it's all your fault. What would you do? And how would you cope?
- Using examples from school and life experiences, explain why you think you would be a good doctor. Do not refer to your work experiences.
- You have given a patient an incorrect dosage. Fortunately, she has not suffered any adverse side effects. She is now asking you why she was given the wrong dosage. What would you say to her, and how would you cope?
- Discuss some research that had a major impact on public health. Why should doctors do research?
- Discuss a time when you had a positive impact on a team. How does this relate to medical school and being a future doctor? Discuss a time you had a negative impact on a team.
- You can donate £1000 to either: a rehabilitation centre, a social care home for the elderly, or a daycare centre for disabled children. Which would you donate to and why? Why do you think we asked you this question?
- Tell me about the skills you learnt from working with people from a different background. How have your experiences helped you to become better suited for a career in medicine?
- What extracurricular activities will make you a good medical student?
- What are the major medical advancements in past 100 years and how have they changed people's lives?
- Scenario: You are the leader of a PBL team. Two of your members have recently split up and are not talking. Other members have complained. What are the issues, and what would you do?
- You are a doctor. On the evening before a patient is due to have a liver transplant, you see him drinking in a pub. What are the issues here, and what would you do?

University of Sunderland Medical School

The medical school is partnered with Keele University School of Medicine.

See Keele Medical School for the MMI stations and questions.

There are 10 stations and only 9 are assessed.
You also have a 30 minutes numeracy test.

They are testing for:
- communication skills,
- what have you done in the community,
- your resilience,
- how you deal with challenges,
- your motivation for medicine,
- current NHS issues,
- what have you done in the community,
- ethical awareness.

You will be emailed a Responsibilities Form which must be completed and returned within the deadline provided.

The form will seek evidence of commitment to work experience, voluntary work, exposure to a caring or supportive roles, the value of the work/role you undertook, the level of responsibility taken in any of the above roles, an example of a situation where you did something that had a significant beneficial outcome for another person, and any exceptional achievements or circumstances.

The form provides an opportunity for you to provide evidence of commitment and personal characteristics appropriate for a future doctor. You'll have an opportunity to discuss your UCAS Personal Statement and your Roles and Responsibilities Form at the Multiple Mini-Interview.

Swansea Medical School

For Graduates only.

You will first sit a 30-minute written situational judgement assessment. This will not assess your academic ability, but try and identify those applicants who have decision making skills suitable to a career in medicine.

You will then attend two separate 20-minute interviews, where your personal statement will be considered and discussed. These are conducted by pairs of interviewers taken from our highly trained panel of clinicians, academics, medical students and members of the public.

The interview process is designed to take account of the personal and academic qualities needed as a doctor, as set out in 'Good Medical Practice', and the capacity to meet the outcomes of 'Outcomes for Graduates'. In summary these are:

- Communication Skills
- Problem solving skills
- Coping with pressure
- Insight and Integrity
- Passion for medicine/resilience to succeed

University College Medical School (BMAT)

It is a traditional interview lasting about 20 minutes. There are usually three interviewers on the panel.

The candidates will be given a copy of their BMAT essay at the beginning of the interview.

They ask several questions about the BMAT essay:

- Why did you not chose one of the other essay topics?
- What was good about your essay, and what not so good?
- How would you improve your essay?
- Why has life expectancy improved dramatically in the last 100 years?
- What makes a good doctor?
- How would your friends describe you?
- What would your friends say is your biggest weakness?
- Give an example of when you've seen leadership in you work experience and in your own personal life
- Explain a medical article as you would to a patient.
- What are the qualities of a good doctor?
- What politics exist between patient and doctor?
- What are the differences between the work of a hospital doctor and a GP?
- What are the frustrations of a GP? What can you offer us?
- How did you get your work experience?
- How is the NHS structured?
- Can you describe a situation that has been stressful?
- How do you cope with stress?
- What makes you angry?

- Why is medical research so important?
- Tell me about some medical advancement you have read about recently.
- How would you deal with angry/distressed patients?
- What do you think you might like best about medicine as a career?
- What do you feel are likely to be the worst thing about being a doctor?
- Why is medicine challenging?
- What difference did your work experience make to you?
- What skills do you have to make you a good doctor?
- How have you dealt with a difficult situation?
- How do you cope in situations where there is not enough time to finish a task?
- How do you deal with conflict?
- Is there much certainty in medicine?
- Do you think it is better for a team of scientists, or an individual scientist to ask the right questions and give the right answers?
- So what are the problems with working in a team? But surely if the team has a strong leader, everyone is just going to follow the leader?
- What do you mean by multidisciplinary team?
- If you saw a colleague making a mistake, would you report them to the manager? What if it was an honest mistake? What problems could that cause in a team?
- Have you been following the news? What happened today?
- What will you bring to UCL?
- What society in particular do you want to get involved in?
- Should doctors be allowed to 'pull the plug' on terminally ill patients?
- Give me an example when you had to show good organisational skills.
- Give us an example when you were in a team when things went wrong, and what did you do about it.
- Why don't you want to be a nurse?
- Some nurses are doing the role of junior doctors in hospitals. How will that affect junior doctors getting experience?
- What aspect of the course here appeals to you?
- When do you become a consultant?
- What will you be doing here, every year, for the next five years?
- What do you think you will find most difficult about a career in medicine?
- What are your strengths and weaknesses?
- Why should we take you and not someone else?
- What three things would you like to change about yourself?

- What is your greatest achievement?
- What would you change about the NHS?
- Would you give a smoker a lung transplant?
- What are the biggest problems facing the NHS?
- What problems do the elderly face and what treatments can doctors offer to the elderly?
- What are the implications for doctors of an increasing ageing population?
- Who is the present health secretary, and if you were stuck in a lift with him what issues would you raise?
- Is it justified to refuse hip operations to obese patients who have no medical reason for their obesity?
- What have you done to prepare yourself for a medical career?
- In your personal statement, you talk about holistic medicine. What do you mean by that?
- When you were on the Stroke Unit during your work experience, how was it important for the doctors to treat the patients holistically?
- So when GPs have only 10 minutes for each patient, do they have enough time to treat them empathetically?
- What do you see yourself doing in six years?
- What has been your greatest non-academic achievement?
- How will the skills you gained from World Challenge help you with a medical career?
- Name a meaningful experience you've had, and how it shaped you.
- What is the latest research into Alzheimers?
- What is the difference between primary, secondary, and tertiary healthcare?
- You are a team leader. Two people in the team aren't getting on with each other but they have to work together because they are the only ones in the team who specialise in those particular areas. How would you go about solving the problem?
- What did you like the most and the least about your work experience?
- Did you see a doctor tell a patient bad news?
- As a doctor, how would you break bad news to a patient. What skills are important here?

University Of East Anglia Medical School. (UEA)

The University of East Anglia uses a seven-station multiple mini interview (MMI). Candidates are given five minutes at each of the stations.

Candidates are assessed on their ability to:
- demonstrate an acceptable approach to decision making when given incomplete or conflicting information
- learn and work effectively in partnership
- show a caring and supportive attitude
- show an empathetic and caring approach
- demonstrate their insight into Medicine as a career and their suitability for the profession
- demonstrate honesty, integrity, and personal effectiveness

Other students were asked:
- What qualities do doctors need?
- Why do doctors need to be resilient? What does resilient mean?
- Why is it important for doctors to de-stress?
- What are your traits and qualities?
- What are you most proud of?
- What are the problems with the NHS?
- When have you done PBL?
- Why Medicine?
- What is a good team?
- What is a bad team?
- When do things go wrong in a team?
- Tell us when you had to make an important decision
- What was your greatest mistake?
- What did you learn from it?
- What would you do differently?
- What is empathy?
- How important is empathy in medicine?
- When have you seen empathy in your work experience?
- When have you shown empathy?
- How do you cope with stress?
- How do you know you are getting stressed?
- Why do doctors get stressed?
- How do doctors behave when they get stressed?
- They had a station on team work and leadership.

- When were you a leader?
- What are the qualities of a team player?
- What are the qualities of a team leader?
- When were you in a bad team?
- What is a bad team?
- What are the advantages and disadvantages of PBL?
- Why is PBL important as a doctor?

A Video Station:
- A medical student accidentally deletes all of her project work. She didn't safe it and doesn't have a copy.
- A medical student in your class has broken up with her boyfriend. She is distraught and is crying.
- A friend's dog is knocked down by a motorist. He raised the dog from a puppy and is distraught.
- The video is stopped at certain stages and you are asked what you would say to the individual in the video.
- Questions on your Personal Statement Station.
- There was one station all on your personal statement.
- 'If a millionaire gives money to charity it may do more harm than good.' Discuss.
- You are asked to read an article on Mental Health, and asked to discuss the issues involved: placement in the community, funding etc.

Warwick Medical School

Graduate only.

Warwick has six MMI Stations lasting around two hours in total. They are looking for:
- Team working
- Insight
- Resilience
- Communication
- Empathy
- Probity
- Respect and Dignity

Personal statement: This station will focus on your work experience.

Other Questions:
- Why do you want to come here?
- Why medicine?
- What did you learn from your work experience?
- What are the challenges of medicine?
- Why did you not apply for medicine before?
- Why is the time right for you to study medicine now?
- Tell us about the course here.

Motivation and insight into medicine: This station will examine how well you have researched medicine as a career. Recent questions asked in the Warwick Medicine interview include the following:
- What have you done to find out about the challenges of working in the healthcare setting?
- What interests you most about our curriculum here?
- Can you tell us about an interesting experience, and what you learned from it about yourself?
- Can you tell us about a significant recent advance in medicine or science?
- Tell us about a book you have read recently and what you enjoyed most about it.
- How important is empathy in medicine?
- When have you showed empathy to a patient?
- Medicine is a popular career. What do you think will be the most rewarding aspects of being a doctor, for you personally?
- Medicine can be challenging. What do you think will be the most challenging aspects for you?
- Following on from that, what strategies or approaches will you use to deal with the challenges you will face here?
- A role play: You see your best friend cheating in his third year medical exam. What would you do?
- Ethical: You are a junior doctor in A&E. A seven-year-old needs a blood transfusion urgently, but the parents will not give consent. They don't want him to have a transfusion. What would you do?
- You are a junior doctor and found out that another doctor did something which you know is wrong and might harm the patients. What would you do?

- Communication: This station will test your communication skills, empathy, honesty, dignity, observation skills etc. You are required to watch a video of a consultation and comment on the effectiveness of the doctor you have observed. Questions have included the following:
- In the video what did the doctor do to communicate effectively with the patient?
- Tell me about a time when you have had to adjust your language and behaviour to help someone understand. What did you adjust and what was the outcome?
- In the video observed, what did the doctor do to show empathy?
- As you know, medical training involves a lot of learning. People have different ways of learning. What techniques do you know of?

More Questions:

- Can you think of a team situation where your communication skills have been vital? Tell us about the situation and how you helped.
- When you were at university, tell us about a situation where you had to work as part of a team and what role did you play?
- When were you a leader and what qualities did you have?
- How important is team work and leadership in medicine?
- How do you deal with stress?
- How do you know when you are getting stressed?
- What are the four ethical principles of medicine?
- Should the NHS do gastric band surgery on the NHS?
- Should Euthanasia become legal?
- What are the attributes of a good doctor?
- What are your experiences of team work and leadership?
- Tell us what can go wrong in a team.
- How do politics influence the NHS?
- If you were given 20 billion pounds to spend on NHS, how would you spend it?
- What are your likely contributions to university life?
- Take us through what you will be doing here, over the next three years.
- What interests you most about our curriculum here?
- Can you tell us about an interesting experience, and what you learned from it about yourself?
- Can you tell us about a significant recent advance in medicine or science?

CHAPTER 20

PRIORITISATION STATIONS

1. On a ward round, the specialty trainee (registrar) tells you to write a drug prescription for a patient. Before prescribing the drug, you realise that this medicine is contra-indicated with the patient's other treatments. The specialty trainee (registrar) has now left the ward.

Rank in order the following actions in response to this situation (1= Most appropriate; 5= Least appropriate)

A. Write up the drug as requested but omit the start date for the drug until you are able to speak to the specialty trainee (registrar)
B. Ask another senior colleague for advice on whether a different drug should be prescribed
C. Decline from prescribing the drug but write in the patient notes that the drug is contra-indicated in this patient
D. Discuss with the ward pharmacist the most appropriate drug to prescribe instead
E. Try to contact the specialty trainee (registrar) to inform him of the patient's other treatments

Answer: EBDCA

Rationale: *This question is assessing how you manage issues of patient safety and how you maintain working relationships. The preferred conduct would be to contact the specialty trainee (registrar)* **(E)**. *This behaviour is likely to result in the safe, simple and rapid resolution of the problem. It will also provide feedback to the specialty trainee (registrar), highlight your own clinical vigilance and maintain an amicable relationship between you and the other team members. It may also be that the medication is only relatively contra-indicated in this situation and that the prescription was not an error. This would therefore provide a learning opportunity for you. The next best option is to seek advice from another senior colleague* **(B)**. *Whilst you are still gaining* *senior advice, this senior colleague may not be familiar with the patient and their background. Discussing with the ward pharmacist **(D)** is the next best option. If a pharmacist recommended a different medication, this should not be prescribed, without consulting with a senior medical team member. This, however, is pro-active and reasonable behaviour. Whilst declining from prescribing the drug and adding to the patient notes **(C)** could be considered safe (ie the patient will not be administered the contra-indicated medication), the underlying issue has not been addressed and is less preferable than consulting a pharmacist which suggests that you are actively trying to resolve the problem. Writing up the drug as requested but omitting the date **(A)** is the least desirable option. This behaviour is potentially dangerous as the medication may well be given in error before you have a chance to speak to your specialty trainee (registrar).*

2. Whilst taking a history from a new patient, she tells you that she was sexually abused by her father as a child but has since come to terms with this. Later she mentions that her father is looking after her eight year old daughter while she is in hospital. You explain that you will have to inform Social Services of the possible risk to her daughter. She says that she would not leave her daughter at risk and insists that the information she has given you remains confidential.

Rank in order the following actions in response to this situation (1= Most appropriate; 5= Least appropriate)

A. Offer to telephone her father to check that her daughter is ok
B. Discuss what you should do with the nurse in charge of the ward
C. Discuss what you should do with your clinical supervisor
D. Explain that it is your duty to discuss this with Social Services as her daughter may be at risk
E. Agree to keep the information confidential but suggest that she try and find alternative caring arrangements for her daughter

Answer: CDBEA

Rationale: *This question assesses your ability to meet your professional duties in a way that is in the interest of the patient at a level that is appropriate for an FY1. In this difficult situation, you should take advice from a senior colleague **(C)**. The GMC states that the disclosure of personal information without consent may be justified when a failure to do so may put the patient* or someone else at risk or disclosure is likely to help in the prevention, detection or prosecution of a serious crime. Though the patient appears to have given you somewhat conflicting information, explaining that you remain concerned about her initial statement about her father and that you have a duty of care and may need to talk with Social Services would be an appropriate option **(D)**. Discussing the situation with the nurse in charge of the ward **(B)** may be helpful but to immediately address the situation Options C and D are preferable. Any immediate and potential risk to the child could be avoided if an alternative carer can be arranged **(E)**, however, this is a less active option and it cannot be assured that this will be effective. Making contact with the father is neither appropriate nor can this offer meaningful reassurance that the child is ok **(A)**.

3. At the morning briefing you are informed by Infection Control that all hospital staff must roll their sleeves up when they have any clinical interaction with patients. During your shift you notice that your FY1 colleague always has her sleeves down.

Rank in order the following actions in response to this situation (1= Most appropriate; 5= Least appropriate)

A. Tell Infection Control that your colleague is not complying with their policy
B. Speak directly to your FY1 colleague about your observation
C. Raise your observation with the nurse in charge of the ward
D. Do not say anything immediately but monitor the situation over the course of the next few days
E. Discuss the situation with your specialty trainee (registrar)

Answer: BECDA

Rationale: *This question is looking at your communication with team members and patient focus. All doctors have a duty to raise concerns where they believe that patient safety is being compromised by the practice of colleagues. However, doctors strive to provide the best care possible to their patients and this situation may have arisen out of some misunderstanding or your FY1 colleague may be concerned about exposing their forearms. It is best therefore to speak directly to your colleague to explore the issue (B). Your specialty trainee (registrar) may be able to help address this situation, though this option is less likely to explain directly the reason for your colleague keeping her sleeves down (E). Other members of the team may be helpful in discussing the* issue (C) but are not in a direct supervisory or management role. Monitoring the situation (D) is less appropriate as it does not immediately address the problem However, it is more appropriate than involving infection control at this stage (A) as this risks damaging your professional relationship with your colleague and does not explore the cause of the problem.

4. It is 8am and you are beginning a New Year's Day shift. A fellow FY1 colleague has called in sick for the same shift stating that she has food poisoning. The following day, you learn that your absent colleague had posted pictures on a social networking site from a New Year's Eve party that she had attended the night before her shift.

Rank in order the following actions in response to this situation (1= Most appropriate; 5= Least appropriate)

A. Make other colleagues on the rota aware of the photos from the party
B. Suggest to your FY1 colleague that she remove the photos from the social networking site
C. Seek advice from another FY1 colleague
D. Ask your colleague for an explanation of why she called in sick the day after a party
E. Alert a senior colleague to the photos on the social networking site

Answer: DCBEA

Rationale: *This question is assessing your ability to work effectively in a team and act in a professional manner. Respect for colleagues is important and there may well be a good explanation for her absence. Indeed she may have got food poisoning at the party; therefore asking your colleague for an explanation is an appropriate first action (D). Seeking advice from colleagues on all aspects of professional life is good practice (C). Doctors should be careful with the use of social networking sites as they are open to the public and can lead to impressions about a doctors fitness to practice e.g. if apparently intoxicated the night before a shift are they fit to work? Removing the photos would be wise (B). Informing a senior colleague would only be the correct action if there was no adequate explanation forthcoming, the doctor did not show genuine remorse and learning or there were ongoing concerns regarding patient safety (E). Advising other colleagues of the photos serves no purpose but to embarrass the individual and is not acceptable (A).*

5. You are just finishing a busy shift on the Acute Assessment Unit (AAU). Your FY1 colleague, who is due to replace you for the evening shift, leaves a message with the nurse in charge that she will be 15 to 30 minutes late. There is only a 30 minute overlap between your timetables to handover to your colleague. You need to leave on time as you have a social engagement to attend with your partner.

Rank in order the following actions in response to this situation (1= Most appropriate; 5= Least appropriate)

A. Make a list of the patients under your care on the AAU, detailing their outstanding issues, leaving this on the notice board in the doctors' office when your shift ends and then leave at the end of your shift ▢
B. Quickly go around each of the patients on the AAU, leaving an entry in the notes highlighting the major outstanding issues relating to each patient and then leave at the end of your shift ▢
C. Make a list of patients and outstanding investigations to give to your colleague as soon as she arrives ▢
D. Ask your specialty trainee (registrar) if you can leave a list of your patients and their outstanding issues with him to give to your colleague when she arrives and then leave at the end of your shift ▢
E. Leave a message for your partner explaining that you will be 30 minutes late

Answer: ECDBA

Rationale: *This question asks you to demonstrate your commitment to patient care. Although it is not appropriate for trainees to stay for an extensive period of time after their shift ends, or do this in a regular basis, staying an extra 30 minutes on this occasion is important to ensure an effective handover (E). It is more appropriate to provide information directly to your colleague to ensure they receive it (C) and your specialty trainee (registrar) could also be able to ensure that your colleague received the information (D). Leaving lists of information on the end of a bed is less effective and leaving a list on the notice board is least effective as your colleague is unlikely to know it is there (B, A).*

6. You have been approached by a FY1 colleague James, who has been on shifts with another FY1 doctor Mark, for the last two weeks. James tells you that Mark has gradually become increasingly careless in monitoring and documenting patient records. On three occasions, James tells you that he has found Mark asleep in the common room whilst on duty. You know Mark very well and have never witnessed such behaviour when you have worked with him previously.

Choose the three most appropriate actions to take in this situation

A. Tell James that you have never witnessed such behaviour from Mark Suggest to James that he speaks to Mark directly about his concerns
B. Advise James to document his concerns
C. Inform a senior colleague about what James has told you
D. Tell James you will speak to Mark about his behaviour Ask other members of the team whether they have witnessed this behaviour in Mark
E. Advise James to speak to a senior colleague about his concerns
F. Ask James whether he has any evidence that patient safety is being compromised

Answer: BGH

Rationale: *This scenario presents a number of conflicts between professional and personal concerns. James should speak directly to Mark about his concerns (B). James has a professional duty to share his concerns with a senior colleague (G), and must do so immediately if he has evidence of patient safety concerns (H). It will be important to keep a professional oversight and not to judge the observations of James (A, C), or act as a third party between James and Mark (D, E, F).*

7. You are reviewing one of your patients, Mrs. Brown, who is on your ward being treated for an infection in her toe. During a routine examination, you notice that in Mrs. Brown's drug chart the FY2 has prescribed her penicillin and the administration is due in 45 minutes time. You remember your consultant informing you earlier that day that Mrs. Brown was allergic to penicillin.

Choose the three most appropriate actions to take in this situation

A. Inform the FY2 that they have made an error
B. Cross out the prescription on Mrs. Brown's drug chart, dating and initialling the amendment
C. Tell the nursing staff on duty not to administer penicillin to Mrs. Brown
D. Contact your specialty trainee (registrar) to confirm what the consultant has said about the penicillin allergy

E. Inform your consultant about the situation
F. Ask Mrs. Brown whether she is allergic to penicillin
G. Explain to Mrs. Brown that an incorrect prescription has been made by the FY2
H. Review Mrs. Brown's notes to try and clarify whether she is allergic to penicillin

Answer: BFH

Rationale: *In this situation you have spotted a possible prescribing error with the potential to result in a fatality or serious injury. Your first duty is to ensure that this danger is eradicated (B). The next priority is to try and establish the facts of the matter by taking a history from the patient (F) and looking for further evidence in the medical notes (H). While it is always appropriate to acknowledge errors to patients, this probable error did not reach the patient and so little is to be gained from explaining the situation to Mrs. Brown (F). While it is always important to explore the causes of 'near misses' with other members of the team (A, E), this discussion is not a priority at this time. If the correct action is taken with regard to the prescribed medicine (B) there should be no need to give specific instructions to the nursing staff (C).*

8. You become aware that one of your FY1 colleagues, Adrian, is consistently not doing his fair share of the ward work. His night shift colleague has told you that he leaves much of the routine work for her and provides poor handover information. However, he is personally very likeable and always performs jobs diligently when directly requested. You know that nobody has approached this with him yet.

Choose the three most appropriate actions to take in this situation.

A. Discuss Adrian's behaviour with his clinical supervisor
B. Suggest to the nursing staff that they ask Adrian directly to complete the routine work
C. Explain to Adrian that his behaviour means colleagues have to do extra work and this could impact on patient safety
D. Bring up the issue of effective handovers at the next team meeting
E. Ask Adrian if he needs help with his handover
F. Discuss the situation with your consultant
G. Ask other staff on the ward if they are experiencing problems with Adrian
H. Suggest to your night shift colleague that she speaks to Adrian directly about him not completing his tasks

Answer: CEH

Rationale: *This question assesses how you manage your professional working relationships and with suboptimal conduct of your colleagues. The most appropriate action is to discuss the issues with Adrian himself (C). Alongside this, it would also be appropriate to offer to help him with his handover (E) as you are therefore attempting to remedy the situation. This is acceptable if this is within your capabilities. Asking the other colleague who is being particularly affected by his behaviour to address him personally (H) before going to his seniors/supervisor would also be considered appropriate.*

Consulting senior medical staff and clinical supervisors (F, A) may well be prudent; however this would be the next step if speaking to him personally was ineffective. The same also goes for gathering further information and opinion on him from the nursing staff (G).

Raising effective handovers at the next team meeting is relatively non-specific and not an immediate priority (D). It is inappropriate to ask the nurses to liaise with him directly regarding routine work (B). The situation needs to be properly addressed and in order for effective and safe patient care, the whole team must be communicating and functioning effectively.

9. You are a new doctor in the accident and emergency department. You realise that you have just administered a vaccine, which is out of date, to a patient. Rank in order the following actions in response to this situation. (1= most appropriate: 5=Least appropriate):

A. Check the expiry dates of all vaccines in the fridge to ensure the other vials are not out of date.
B. Inform the patient what has happened and reassure him not to worry as the vaccine is only three months out of date.
C. Inform the patient what has happened and apologise. Monitor the patient for any signs of them developing a reaction and tell them to return to hospital if any adverse effects occur.
D. Fill out a critical incident form.
E. Do not say anything to the patient.

Answer DCAEB.

This is definitely your error and you didn't take responsibility to check the expiry date of the vaccine. It is always the best practice to be honest with the patient and check with a senior colleague whether the patient will need a further dose to provide maximum protection. To prevent this happening in the future and to protect patients, it is important to check the expiry dates of all the vaccines in the fridge and also to fill out a critical incident form to prevent future occurrences, and for the records.

10. A 45-year-old alcoholic, who stopped drinking two days previously, is admitted with delirium in the afternoon. During the night, you are called to see him as he has become very aggressive and is demanding to be allowed home. As you arrive on the ward, he punches one of the nurses. He is confused, shouting and threatening other patients.

Choose the three most appropriate actions to take in this situation

A. Prescribe extra sedation for the patient.
B. Ask the nursing staff to call hospital security.
C. Attempt to talk to the patient to try and calm him down.
D. Reassure the other patients in the ward that they are safe.
E. Ask the nursing staff to help you restrain the patient.
F. Ask the nursing staff to call the police.
G. Inform the patient that his behaviour is inappropriate and will not be tolerated.
H. Ensure that the nurse who was punched is not seriously injured.

Answer: BCH

Rationale: *This question assesses your ability to cope with pressure and ensure the safety of yourself and other patients. Violence against health professionals (and patients) is not acceptable, but for this patient it is in the context of delirium tremens, in which the patient is confused and agitated, so he would not have insight into his actions. Hence Options G and F are not appropriate. However, an FY1 (or another member of staff) should be protected and hospital security (B) can offer assistance. Even though a patient is confused, they will often calm down if approached in a reasonable manner, reducing the emotion in the situation (C). An FY1 also has a duty to ensure the safety of other staff, so checking on any harm done is important (H). Physically restraining the patient will be difficult and might cause further harm for staff and the patient. It can constitute an assault. Similarly, prescribing extra sedation might exacerbate the confusion and would likely be very difficult to administer without first calming the patient down. Consequently Options A and E are not appropriate.*

(Some of the above was taken from Warwick.ac.uk and the Medical School Council.)

41 EXAMPLES OF ETHICAL DILEMMA QUESTIONS
(See Chapter 7)

1 Notifiable disease
2 Assisted Suicide/Euthanasia
3 Prescribing Oral Contraceptive Pill
4 Treatment of Obese/Smokers
5 Obese Patient Demanding Hip Replacement
6 Patient Confidentiality
7 Professional Boundaries
8 Doctor Behaviour
9 Definition of "Competent"
10 Patient Choice
11 Request for Non-Conventional Treatment
12 Request for Husband's Sperm
13 Request for Expensive Prescription
14 Disclosure of Diagnosis
15 Abortion
16 Right to Die
17 Surrogacy
18 Difference of Opinion regarding Right to Live
19 Exposure to HIV
20 Organ Transplant
21 Blood Transfusion
22 Disclosure of Genetic Condition
23 Gillick Competence
24 Abortion
25 Abortion
26 Patient Demanding Antibiotics
27 Refusal to Take Medication
28 Vaccinations
29 Confidentiality

ANNEX 2

30 EXAMPLES OF ROLE PLAYING SCENARIOS
(See Chapter 8)

1 Dry Cleaning Error
2 Request to Forge Signature for a Friend
3 Injured Friend
4 Friend Cheating
5 Finding Syringes at home
6 Overdose
7 Sharing Library Card
8 Classmate Skipping Classes
9 Weight Problem
10 Forging Signature
11 Prescription with Allergic Reaction
12 Drunk Student
13 Consultant Smelling of Alcohol
14 Fear of Flying
15 Team Member not Pulling his Weight
16 Speaking to a Patient with Epilepsy
17 Colleague Faking Illness
18 Patient given wrong Vaccine
19 Issuing Doctor's Note
20 How would you deal with an angry patient?
21 Mistake
22 Colleague Consistently Late
23 Colleague with Cocaine Addiction
24 Social Networking Sites
25 Drunk Patient
26 Complaint about Standard of Care
27 Accidental Needle Injury to Self
28 Request from Colleague for Prescription
29 Suspect Colleague Possesses Cocaine
30 Collaboration Station

44 EXAMPLES OF MMI PERSONAL SKILLS (SEE CHAPTER 9)

1 Leadership
2 Team Player
3 Personal Description
4 What are your strengths/weaknesses?
5 Personal Qualities
6 Team Work
7 Leadership
8 Are you a leader or a follower?
9 Leadership and Mistakes
10 Time Management
11 Multi-Tasking
12 Team Player Example
13 What is Resilience?
14 What can go wrong in a team?
15 MMI Personal Skill Station: Describe a challenge you have overcome.
16 Conflict Management
17 Accomplishments
18 Commitment
19 Why Medicine?
20 Multi-Disciplinary Team
21 Team Players
22 Compassion
23 Personal Description
24 Organization Skills
25 Team Work
26 What makes a good Team
27 Personal Qualities
28 Reaction to Failure
29 Positives and Negatives

ANNEX 4

19 EXAMPLES OF MMI WORK EXPERIENCE QUESTIONS
(SEE CHAPTER 10)

1 What did you learn from your work experience?
2 Nursing Home
3 Nursing Home
4 Hospice
5 Work Experience Abroad
6 Challenges of India
7 GP Experience
8 Role of the Patient
9 Disabled Patient
10 Communication
11 Motivation for Medicine
12 Team Working/Shadowing
13 Personal Statement
14 Shadowing a Cardiologist
15 Shadowing in A&E
16 GP Practice
17 Challenges of Work Experience
18 Holistic Medicine
19 Useful Skills

20 EXAMPLES OF MMI KNOWLEDGE QUESTIONS (SEE CHAPTER 11)

1 Barriers to Doctor/Patient Communication
2 Uncertainty in Medicine
3 What is a diagnosis?
4 Inequalities in Healthcare
5 When would a doctor lie to a patient?
6 Junior Doctors
7 Factors affecting health or population
8 History of Medicine
    (a) Over the last 10 years
    (b) Over the last 50 years.
    (c) 100 years ago
9 Becoming a Consultant
10 Putting Someone off Medicine
11 Six Core Values of NHS
12 Medical Treatments in Hospital or Community
13 Politics influencing Healthcare
14 NHS Problems
15 Funding of Healthcare
16 Bariatric Surgery
17 Promoting Good Health
18 Change of Career Path
19 What is the Structure of NHS?
20 What are the duties of a doctor?

6 EXAMPLES OF MMI COMMUNICATION QUESTIONS (SEE CHAPTER 12)

1 Train Crash
2 Mistake leading to Patient Death
3 Friend over Alcohol Limit
4 Rude Consultant
5 Telling a Patient Bad News
6 Surgeon Over the Alcohol Limit

MORE GENERAL QUESTIONS

1. What does the term inequality in medicine mean to you?
2. You are a GP –one of your patients has recently split from her fiancé just before they were scheduled to emigrate to Canada. She wants a medical certificate from you, to say that she in unwell. You are now going to discuss this patient with the GP supervisor.
3. You share a flat with a boy called Sam. You have noticed some marks on his arms, some of which look new – you are worried that he is self-harming. You are very concerned and so have arranged to meet him for coffee to discuss the issue. Explain what you might say.
4. You are a leader of a group that is working on a project. One member does not show up at the meetings and does not contribute to the team at all. What might be the reasons for him not showing up or contributing? What options do you have as a team leader to resolve the issue? What are the advantages and disadvantages of each option? How would you go about resolving the issue?
5. A patient arrives in casualty but claims to only want to be examined by his GP, what would you do?
6. You have to choose one of your course mates as a treasurer for a party you are organising. Who out of the following would you choose and why? Why not choose the others?
   a. Tim is a friendly guy who everyone gets on well with but he is currently failing in his numeracy course.
   b. Amy is a show off and brags about her excellent marks, no one likes her much.
   c. Sophie has been cautioned for shoplifting and is trying to show her tutor that she is trustworthy.
7. You have handed in an essay which you worked really hard on and expect an excellent mark. Instead, your mark was very poor and you are upset because you think your tutor is failing you on purpose. How do you approach the situation?
   a. Compare your essay with the one your friend wrote and see where you were marked down

    b.   Go to your tutor and complain about your mark, pointing out how unfair it is and how hard you prepared for it

    c.   Go to another tutor who you think sympathises with you and complain about your mark, asking for a second opinion

    d.   None of the above (Explain what you would do and why)

8. You are captain of a sinking ship and you can only save one of the following. Who would you chose and why?

    a.   A young gay man who looks after his mother who has Alzheimer's disease. He is also the manager of a company with 30 employees.

    b.   A teenage mother who has a little girl. She used to be a drug addict and now suffers from depression.

    c.   A forty-year-old man with Down's Syndrome who lives alone with a cat and rabbit and works in a charity shop.

9. A young woman presents with rheumatoid arthritis. She has tried all of the conventional treatments but is still having problems. Unless her symptoms improve she will have to give up work in the near future. The tutor tells you that there is a new, but very expensive treatment available. Treatment for a single patient costs as much as conventional treatment for 12 patients. The drug is not effective in all patients and in all patients and in some cases gives rise to a worsening of the symptoms. What do you do?

10. Is medicine an art or a science?

11. Should people who indulge in extreme sports and get injured expect the NHS to treat them for free?

12. A patient has been seriously assaulted by her partner. You fear for her safety but she refuses to report it to the police. What would you do?

13. Is it unethical for people to receive better treatment just because they can afford private health care?

14. I am from overseas. Please tell me about the NHS?

15. One of your flat mates from the year below has copied a piece of your work and submitted it as her own, knowing that the person who marked your work has now left the university. What would you do?

16. If a patient is unconscious and an operation is needed urgently, is consent needed and from whom?

17. The patient decides to choose the no treatment route but tells you that he does not want you to tell her husband. What are the ethical issues here?

18. A man refuses treatment for a potentially life-threatening condition. What are the ethical issues here?